Brains, Machines and Mathematics

Michael A. Arbib

McGraw-Hill Book Company
New York San Francisco Toronto London

Brains, Machines, and Mathematics

First McGraw-Hill Paperback Edition, 1965

Library of Congress Catalog Card Number 63-21473

McGraw-Hill Paperbacks

To Fred Pollock for teaching mathematics wisely, wittily, and well

Preface

This book forms an *introduction* to the common ground of brains, machines, and mathematics, where mathematics is used to exploit analogies between the working of brains and the control-computation-communication aspects of machines. It is designed for a reader who has heard of such currently fashionable topics as cybernetics, information theory, and Gödel's theorem and wants to gain from one source more of an understanding of them than is afforded by popularizations. Here the reader will find not only *what* certain results are, but also *why*. The number of pages has been deliberately kept small so that a first reading is feasible in an evening or two. Yet a lot of ground is covered, and the reader who wants to go further should find himself reasonably well prepared to tackle the technical literature. Full use of the book does require a moderate mathematical background—a year of college calculus (or the equivalent "mathematical maturity"). However, much of the book should be intelligible to the reader who chooses to skip the mathematical proofs, and no previous study of biology or computers is required at all.

Before reviewing the contents, I should say a few words as to the present status of neurophysiology and the nature of our model making.

The use of microelectrodes, electron microscopes, and radioactive tracers has yielded a huge increase in neurophysiological knowledge in the past few decades. Even a multivolume work such as the "Handbook of Neurophysiology" cannot fully cover all the facts. Many neurophysiological theories, once widely held, are being questioned as improved techniques reveal finer structures and more sophisticated chemicoelectrical cellular mechanisms. This means that our presentation of mathematical models in this book will have to be based on a grossly simplified view of the brain and the central nervous system. The reader may well begin to wonder what value or interest the study of such systems can have.

There is a variety of properties—memory, computation, learning, purposiveness, reliability despite component malfunction—which it might seem difficult to attribute to "mere mechanisms." However, herein lies one important reason for our study: By making mathematical models, we have proved that there do exist purely electrochemical mechanisms which have the above properties. In other words, we have helped to "banish the ghost from the machine." We may not *yet* have modeled *the* mechanisms that the brain employs, but we have at least modeled *possible* mechanisms, and that in itself is a great stride forward.

There is another reason for such a study, and it goes much deeper. Many of the most spectacular advances in *physical* science have come from the wedding of the mathematicodeductive method and the experimental method. The mathematics of the last 300 years has grown largely out of the needs of physics—applied mathematics directly, and pure mathematics indirectly by a process of abstraction from applied mathematics (often for purely esthetic reasons far removed from any practical considerations). In these pages we coerce what is essentially still the mathematics of the physicist to help our slowly dawning comprehension of the brain and its electromechanical analogs. It is probable that the dim beginnings of *biological* mathematics here discernible will one day happily bloom into new and exciting systems of pure mathematics. Here, however, we *apply* mathematics to derive far-reaching conclusions from clearly stated premisses. We can test the adequacy of a model of the brain by expressing it in mathematical form and using our mathematical tools to prove general theorems. In the light of any discrepancies we find between these theorems and experiments, we may return to our premisses and reformulate them, thus gaining a deeper understanding of the workings of the brain. Further, such theories can guide us in building more useful and sophisticated machines.

The beauty of this mathematicodeductive method is that it allows us to *prove* general properties of our models and thus affords a powerful adjunct to model making in the wire and test-tube sense.

Biological systems are so much more complicated than the

usual systems of physics that we cannot expect to achieve a fully satisfactory *biological* mathematics for many years to come. However, the quest is a very real and important one. This book strives to introduce the reader to its early stages. He will, I hope, find that the results so far obtained are of interest. Certainly they represent only a very minute fraction of what remains to be found —but the start of a quest is nonetheless exciting for being the start. I do not believe that the application of mathematics will solve all our physiological and psychological problems. What I do believe, though, is that the mathematicodeductive method must take an important place beside the experiments and clinical studies of the neurophysiologist and the psychologist in our drive to understand brains, just as it has already helped the electrical engineer to build the electronic computers which, though many, many degrees of magnitude less sophisticated than biological organisms, still represent our closest man-made analog to brains.

We can now review the scope of this book:

We will first take a very quick look at neurophysiology, and from this we will formulate our crude first model of the brain as a network of components called McCulloch-Pitts neurons. We will see that anything an electronic computer can do can be done by such a network. We shall study the relation of these networks with finite automata and Turing machines; review work on the visual system of the frog as an example of complicated brain structure; and study the Perceptron (a machine that "learns"). We shall then review neurological evidence for neuron malfunction. This review will stress the need to understand how to design networks which function reliably despite component malfunction. After a glance at the early von Neumann approach, we shall study Shannon's communication theory. We shall then be able to consider the Cowan-Winograd solution to the problem of reliable design. Then we turn to the study of Norbert Wiener's cybernetics—the study of control and communication in the animal and the machine. We shall examine the fundamental concept of feedback and the resultant insights gained into the functioning of the nervous system. We then take Greene's scheme of resonant frequencies in neural nets as an antidote to a too-ready identification of real brains with McCulloch-Pitts neural nets. After a discussion of homeostasis and prosthesis, we shall turn to Gestalt and the recognition of universals—how we perceive auditory and visual forms. The final chapter will be devoted to Gödel's incompleteness theorem. We shall give a historical outline of the trends in mathematical thought which led up to Gödel's work, prove the theorem, discuss its dramatic philosophical consequences for the foundations of mathematics, and finally look at its role in the brain-machine controversy.

This book is a revision of the lecture notes of a course delivered in June–August of 1962 at the University of New South Wales in Sydney, Australia. I want to thank John Blatt for inviting me to the Visiting Lectureship; Derek Broadbent for inviting me to broadcast the lectures; and Joyce Kean for her superb job of typing up the original lecture notes.

I have spent the last two years with the Research Laboratory of Electronics and the Department of Mathematics at the Massachusetts Institute of Technology on a research assistantship (supported by the U.S. Armed Forces and National Institute of Health). I owe so many debts of gratitude to the people there that I cannot fully do justice to them. However, I do particularly want to thank Warren McCulloch for his continual help and encouragement. It was George W. Zopf who first urged publication of the lectures. Bill Kilmer gave the original lecture notes a helpful and critical reading. For years I have nurtured the desire to claim at a point such as this, "Any mistakes which remain are thus solely his responsibility." However, this would be a sorry expression of a very genuine gratitude, and so I follow convention and admit that any errors which remain are my responsibility.

Finally, I should like to thank all those authors whose work I have quoted and their publishers for so graciously granting me permission to use their material.

Michael A. Arbib

Contents

1

Neural Nets, Finite Automata, and Turing Machines

1.1 Introductory Neurophysiology

I want to start by giving a very sketchy account of neurophysiology—merely sufficient as a basis for our first mathematical model. We may regard the nervous system of man as a three-stage system as shown in Fig. 1.1.†

Our fundamental hypothesis in setting up our model is that all the functioning of the nervous system relevant to our study is mediated solely by the passage of electrical impulses by cells we call neurons. Actually, the human brain contains more *glial* cells than it contains *neurons*. Until recently, it was neurophysiological orthodoxy to believe that these glial cells served only to support and nourish the neurons—functions irrelevant to our study. However, the last 15 years have seen a growing number support the view that the

† The purpose of the arrows drawn from right to left will be made clear in the discussion of feedback in Sec. 4.1.

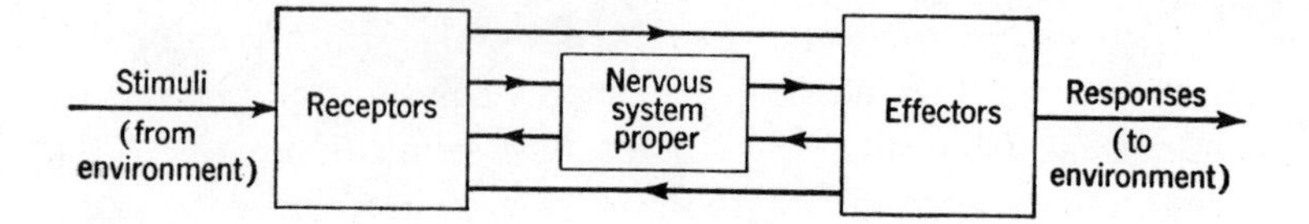

Figure 1.1 The nervous system of man considered as a three-stage system.

glial cells actually carry out functions, such as memory, which are of interest here. Throughout this book, we shall ignore such posited glial functions. We shall also ignore such modes of neural interaction as continuously variable potentials and transmission of hormones. In setting up our *possible* mechanisms, neural impulses will fully suffice—*future developments will, of course, require the ascription of far greater importance to the other neural functions and perhaps to the glia.*

In the light of our fundamental hypothesis, then, we shall simply view the nervous system proper as a vast network of neurons, arranged in elaborate structures with extremely complex interconnections. This network receives inputs from a vast number of receptors: the rods and cones of the eyes, the pain, touch, hot, and cold receptors of the skin, the stretch receptors of the muscles, etc., all converting stimuli from the body or the external world into patterns of electrical impulses which convey information into the network. These interact with the enormously complicated patterns already traveling through the neurons (there are estimated to be 10^{10} neurons in the neural net which is the human brain!) and result in the emission of impulses which control the effectors, such as our muscles and glands, to give our responses. Thus we have our three-stage system: receptors, neural net, and effectors.

We are not going to formulate models of the receptors or effectors here, but we do want a model of the neural net. To do this, we shall first model the neuron. The neurons of our nervous system come in many forms, but we shall restrict our study to neurons like that of Fig. 1.2.

The *neuron* is a cell and so has a nucleus, which is contained in the *soma* or *body* of the cell. One may think of the *dendrites* as a very fine filamentary bush, each fiber being thinner than the axon, and of the *axon* itself as a long, thin cylinder carrying

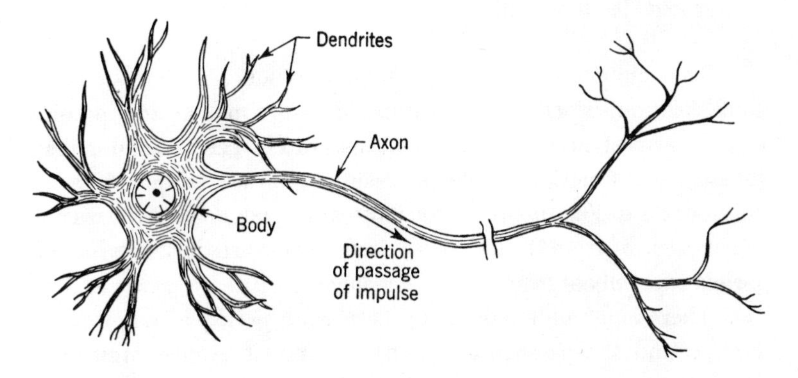

Figure 1.2 Schematic drawing of a neuron.

impulses from the soma to other cells. The axon splits into a fine arborization, each branch of which finally terminates in a little *endbulb* almost touching the dendrites of a neuron. Such a place of near contact is called a *synapse.* Impulses reaching a synapse set up graded electrical signals in the dendrites† of the neuron on which the synapse impinges, the interneuronal transmission being sometimes electrical and sometimes by diffusion of chemicals. A particular neuron will only fire an electrical impulse along its axon if sufficient impulses reach the endbulbs impinging on its dendrites in a short period of time, called the *period of latent summation.* Actually, these impulses may either help or hinder the firing of an impulse and are correspondingly called *excitatory* or *inhibitory.* The condition for the firing of a neuron is then that the excitation should exceed the inhibition by a critical amount called the *threshold of the neuron.* If we assign a suitable positive weight to

† A synapse may also occur on other axons. This "interaction of afferents" is discussed in Sec. 3.1.

each excitatory synapse and a negative weight to each inhibitory synapse, we can say that

a neuron fires only if the total weight of the synapses which receive impulses in the period of latent summation exceeds the threshold (1.1.1)

This picture of simple linear summation is, again, a gross simplification. Further, the threshold is a time-varying parameter—however, this time variance has rarely been considered in formal neuron modeling and plays no part in the models we shall consider here. The reader who is close to despair at this ever-widening departure from reality is advised to re-read the introduction for encouragement!

There is a small time delay between a period of latent summation and the passage of the corresponding axonal impulse to its endbulbs, so that the arrival of impulses on the dendrites of a neuron determines the firing of its axon at a slightly later time.

After an impulse has traveled along an axon, there is a time called the *refractory period* during which the axon is incapable of transmitting an impulse. Hence, during a length of time equal to one refractory period, at most one impulse may be fired along the axon. If we now choose as our unit of time the refractory period of the neuron, we may specify the firing behavior of our neuron by specifying for each of the first, second, third, etc., time intervals whether or not the neuron fired. We are thus led to the simplifying assumption that our neuron (already far removed from reality) may only fire at times $t = 1, 2, 3, 4, \ldots$ units of time after some suitable origin. We next make the *gross* assumption that we may use the same *discrete time scale* for all the neurons of our net. That is, we assume the firing behavior of our net is completely specified by the firing pattern of the individual neurons at the discrete times $t = 1, 2, 3, \ldots$. In line with this, we assume that the axonal firing of a neuron is determined by the firing pattern of inputs at its synapses one moment of our discrete time scale earlier.

1.2 The McCulloch-Pitts Model

The highly simplified neurophysiological considerations of the last section lead to the McCulloch-Pitts model of the neuron:

Definition 1.2.1 A *module* (or *formal neuron*) is an element with, say, m inputs $x_1, \ldots, x_m$ $(m \geq 1)$ and one output d. It is characterized by $m + 1$ numbers, its threshold θ, and the weights $w_1, \ldots, w_m$, where w_i is associated with x_i. The module operates on a discrete time scale $t = 1, 2, 3, 4, \ldots,$ the firing of its output at time $n + 1$ being determined by the firing of its inputs at time n according to the following rule (cf. Statement 1.1.1): The module fires an impulse along its axon at time $n + 1$ if and only if the total weight of the inputs stimulated at time n exceeds the threshold of the neuron.

If we introduce the symbolism

$m(t) = 0$ for "m does not fire at time t"
$m(t) = 1$ for "m does fire at time t"

(where m may be an axonal output or a synaptic input of a neuron), we see that the above rule may be expressed symbolically as

$$d(n + 1) = 1 \qquad \text{if and only if } \Sigma w_i x_i(n) \geq \theta$$

Note that a positive weight $w_i > 0$ corresponds to an excitatory synapse (i.e., module input) whereas a negative weight $w_i < 0$ means that x_i is an inhibitory input.

In terms of this very simple model of a neuron, we may immediately define our first model of a neural net:

Definition 1.2.2 A *modular net* is a collection of modules, each with the same time scale, interconnected by splitting the output of any module into a number of lines and connecting some or all of these to the inputs of other modules. An output may thus lead to any number of inputs, but an input may only come from at most one output.

The *input lines* of a net are those inputs $l_0, l_1, \ldots, l_{m-1}$ of modules of the net which are not connected to modular outputs. The *output lines* of a net are those lines $p_0, p_1, \ldots, p_{r-1}$ from modular outputs which are not connected to modular inputs.

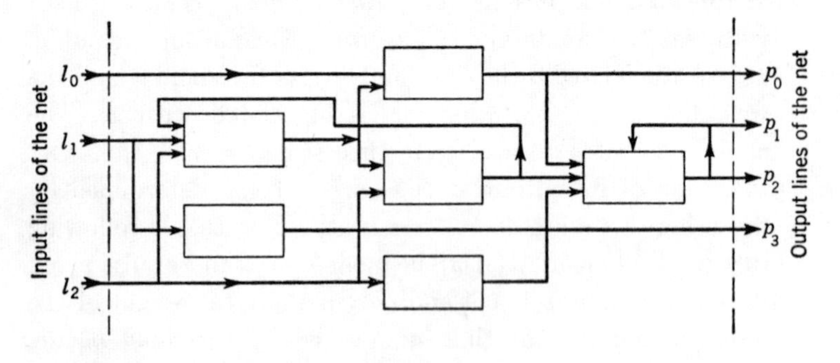

Figure 1.3 A simple modular net.

In the example of Fig. 1.3, there are three input lines and four output lines—note that the input lines may split and that the output lines need not come from distinct modules.

We have now set up a model of the brain. To the reader who thinks of a model as an actual collection of wires and transistors, my use of the word "model" here may seem somewhat strange. Therefore, let me stress that throughout this book, the word is used in the mathematical sense. The *engineer* feels he has modeled a system when he has actually constructed an apparatus which he can hope will behave similarly to the original system. The *mathematician*, on the other hand, feels that he has modeled a system when he has "captured" some properties of the system in precise mathematical definitions and axioms in such a form that he can deduce further properties of this "formal" (i.e., mathematical) *model;* thus, hopefully, *explaining* known properties of the original system and *predicting* new properties. The concept of a "modular net" has a precise mathematical definition (and we shall prove theorems about it in subsequent sections), and it is in this mathematical sense that we consider it to be a model of the brain. Before we study it, let us stress that *we have only obtained it at the cost of drastic simplifications:*

a. We have assumed complete synchronization of all the neurons.
b. We have fixed the threshold and weights of each neuron for all time.
c. We have ignored the effects of hormones and chemicals (e.g., alcohol) in changing the behavior of the brain.
d. We have ignored all interaction between neurons (e.g., due to the electrical field associated with their impulses) save that taking place at the synapses.
e. We have ignored the glial cells.

The list can be extended, and it must be realized that *our first model is only a starting point for our study and not an end in itself*. However, our simplifications have not rendered our model completely powerless, and a modular network can indeed store information and carry out computations. We shall demonstrate this in Sec. 1.4 by "blueprinting" a digital computer as a modular network. First, however, we shall use Sec. 1.3 to introduce the concept of "finite automaton" and relate it to that of "modular network"; while in Sec. 1.7 we shall consider a trivial model of perception by giving a mathematical characterization of the dichotomies which may be made of its input sequences by a finite automaton.

1.3 Finite Automata and Modular Nets

In this section, we introduce the concept of finite automaton in such a way as to make it clear that every modular net is a finite automaton. Our objective will then be to show that, conversely, the input-output behavior of a finite automaton can always be carried out by a suitably constructed modular net. Since it is much easier, in general, to design a finite automaton for a given task than to design the corresponding modular net, the result clarifies for us what tasks our modular nets are capable of performing (cf. Sec. 1.4).

Let the modular net N have g modules, m input lines, and r output lines.

We say that we know the *input* of the net when we know which of the input lines are on and which are off—there are thus 2^m inputs, since we can assign the values "on" and "off" to the m input lines in 2^m different ways. Similarly, we have 2^r *outputs.*

We say that we know the *state* of the net at time t if we know which of the modules are firing and which are not firing at that time. Thus there are 2^g states.

We denote by S the set of states, by I the set of inputs, and by O the set of outputs of our net N.

The firing of a module of N at time $t + 1$ is determined by the firing pattern of the module's inputs at time t and so, a fortiori, is determined by the state and input of the whole net N at time t. But this means that *the input and state of the net at time t determine the output and state of the net at time* $t + 1$. Hence we can now define a "finite automaton" as an easy generalization of a modular net. We will regard a finite automaton as a "black box" which can accept any of a finite number of inputs, which has a finite number of "internal states" (be they the states of a modular net or the positrons of the cogs in a piece of clockwork), and which can emit any of a finite number of outputs. As above, we assume that *the input and state at time t determine the output and state at time* $t + 1$. We express these requirements mathematically as follows:

Definition 1.3.1 A *finite automaton* is a quintuple

$$A = (I,O,S,\lambda,\delta)$$

where I is a finite set (the set of inputs)
O is a finite set (the set of outputs)
S is a finite set (the set of internal states)
$\lambda: S \times I \rightarrow S$ is the next-state function†
$\delta: S \times I \rightarrow O$ is the next-output function

† The reader unfamiliar with any of these and subsequent notations should consult the Appendix.

We then consider A to work on a discrete time scale, so that if at time t it is in state q and receives input a, then at time $t + 1$ it has changed to state $\lambda(q,a)$ and emits output $\delta(q,a)$.

Clearly, then, *any modular net is a finite automaton.* What is surprising is that any finite automaton can, essentially, be replaced by a modular net. The details of this replacement are not at all profound, and the reader who is not interested in them may skip straight to Sec. 1.4.

If our finite automaton A has m possible inputs $i_0, \ldots, i_{m-1}$ and r possible outputs $o_0, \ldots, o_{r-1}$, we construct a modular net N with m *input lines* $h_0, \ldots, h_{m-1}$ (note that N thus has 2^m *inputs*) and r output lines $p_0, \ldots, p_{r-1}$. We associate the input i_j to A with the input $\bar{\imath}_j$ of N in which the only input line which fires is h_j. Similarly, we define an output $\bar{o}_j$ of N. Our desired net N then comprises nr modules labeled (k,j) corresponding to state k and input i_j of our automaton A, and m modules labeled (k) corresponding to output o_k. Output line p_k of our net N is taken from the module (k).

We arrange our connections so that the module (k,j) is on at time $t + 1$ if and only if the automaton A was in the kth state and received the input i_j at time t; and the module (k) is on at time $t + 1$ if and only if the automaton A emits output o_k at time t.

Let $\{k_1,k_2, \ldots, k_{n(k)}\} = \{(i,j) \mid \lambda(i,j) = k\}$, i.e., these are the *state-input* pairs which send the automaton A into the kth *state.*

Then the module (k,l) is to have the function $(k,l)(t + 1)$ if and only if $h_l(t) \wedge [k_1(t) \vee \ldots \vee k_{n(k)}(t)]$.† That is, it fires at time $(t + 1)$ if and only if the state of A at time t is to be the kth, and the input to A at time t is the lth.

Let $\{\bar{k}_1,\bar{k}_2, \ldots, \bar{k}_{m(k)}\} = \{(i,j) \mid \delta(i,j) = k\}$, i.e., these are the state-input pairs which cause the automaton A to emit the kth *output.*

Then the module (k) is to have the function $(k)(t + 1)$ if and only if $\bar{k}_1(t) \vee \ldots \vee \bar{k}_{m(k)}(t)$.

† Symbolism: $\wedge$ for "and"; $\vee$ for "or." Note also that here $k_1(t)$ is to be read "k_1 fires at time t," etc.

You may check that each module can indeed be obtained by suitable choice of weights and threshold. We can see now that our net N satisfies the following theorem:

Theorem 1.3.1 Let $A = (I,O,S,\lambda,\delta)$ be any finite automaton:

$I = \{i_0, \ldots, i_{m-1}\}$
$O = \{o_0, \ldots, o_{r-1}\}$
$S = \{s_0, \ldots, s_{q-1}\}$

Then there exists a neural net N, subsets $\{\bar{i}_0, \ldots, \bar{i}_{m-1}\}$ of its inputs, $\{\bar{o}_0, \ldots, \bar{o}_{r-1}\}$ of its outputs, and $\{\bar{s}_0, \ldots, \bar{s}_{q-1}\}$ of its states such that if input $i_{j_1}, \ldots, i_{j_n}$ to A initially in state s_j yields output $o_{k_1}, \ldots, o_{k_n}$, then input $\bar{i}_{j_1}, \ldots, \bar{i}_{j_n}$ to N initially in state $\bar{s}_j$ yields output $\bar{o}_{k_1}, \ldots, \bar{o}_{k_n}$ (with a delay of at most one time unit).

What this overelaborate piece of symbolism means is simply that the input-output behavior of a finite automaton can always be replaced by a restriction of the input-output behavior of a modular net.

1.4 Finite Automata and Digital Computers

Recalling the fact (shown in Sec. 1.3) that any finite automaton can be replaced by a modular net, it is now easy to demonstrate the capability of a modular net for memory and computation. We do this by constructing a digital computer† from interconnected finite automata—for we then know that (perhaps after a little juggling with delays) we can replace these automata by a modular network. A digital computer provided with programs (lists of instructions) of 1964 vintage is, of course, a far less "intelligent" object‡ than a brain provided with an education of 1964

† There are two principal varieties of computer—analog and digital. We only discuss digital computers here.

‡ However, there already exist programs which enable computers to exhibit aspects of "intelligent" behavior—a brief description of two of these is given in Sec. 4.5.

vintage—here we merely show that our initial brain model, crude as it is, at least subsumes these computers.

An ordinary digital computer usually comprises four units: an input-output unit, a store, a logic (i.e., logical control) unit, and an arithmetic unit. The input-output unit serves to read instructions and data off a tape input and transfer them to the store and, conversely, to transfer the results of computations from the store to a tape output. The store contains a finite number of "pigeonholes" each with an address, and each holding one "word"—where the "word" may be either a number (data, or of use in computation, or result) or an instruction. The logic unit takes one instruction at a time from the store and executes it. If it is an input-output or refer-to-memory operation, it actuates the input-output unit or store; if an arithmetic operation, the arithmetic unit; if a branch operation, it carries out a test to decide on its next instruction.

For definiteness, let us consider a computer whose instructions comprise an operation command followed by three store addresses:

Op Operand 1 Operand 2 Next Instruction

The first two addresses tell the logic unit where to find its operands (i.e., its data), the last tells where to find the next instruction. For example, one might have

ADD 3275 3119 4006

to be interpreted: Add the numbers stored at addresses 3275 and 3119 and then execute the instruction stored at address 4006. We now describe the automata.

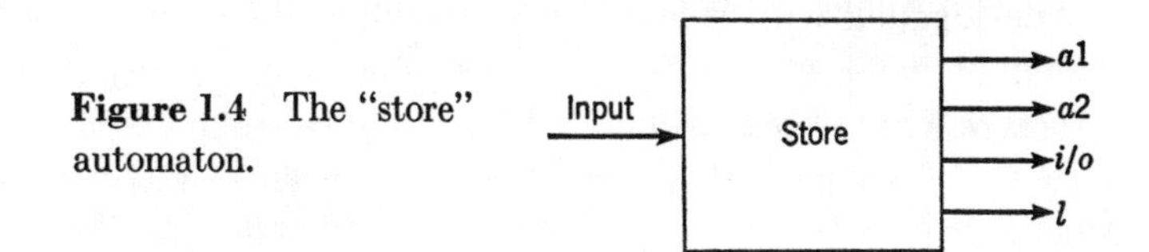

Figure 1.4 The "store" automaton.

The state of the *store*, Fig. 1.4, when it contains the words $x_1, \ldots, x_n$ in its n "pigeonholes" is simply labeled $(x_1, \ldots, x_n)$. The inputs are of the form (m,b,o) and (m,o,d). Input (m,b,o)

causes the word b to be stored at address m; i.e., its state changes from $(x_1, \ldots, x_{m-1}, x_m, x_{m+1}, \ldots, x_n)$ to $(x_1, \ldots, x_{m-1}, b, x_{m+1}, \ldots, x_n)$, and there is no output. The store has four output lines, two to the arithmetic unit, one to the input-output unit, and one to the logic unit, $a1$, $a2$, i/o, and l, respectively. Input (m,o,d) causes the word with address m to be transferred along the d-output line (where d is $a1$, $a2$, i/o, or l) to the appropriate unit; i.e., state $(x_1, \ldots, x_m, \ldots, x_n)$ remains unchanged and x_m is sent out along the d output. The store is clearly a finite automaton.

The *arithmetic unit* (Fig. 1.5) has three input lines, one (Op) from the logic unit and two ($a1$ and $a2$) from the store. It

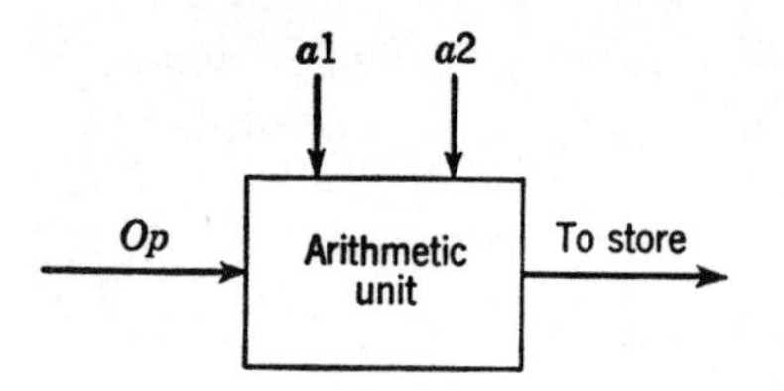

Figure 1.5 The "arithmetic unit" automaton.

comprises two registers, and their contents B_1 and B_2 fix the state (B_1,B_2) of the unit. The inputs are triplets $(Op,a1,a2)$. Input $(O,a1,O)$ causes $a1$ to be stored in the first register: (B_1,B_2) changes to $(a1,B_2)$, and there is no output. Similarly, $(O,O,a2)$ changes (B_1,B_2) to $(B_1,a2)$. Input (Op,O,O) causes the computation Op to be carried out on (B_1,B_2) to form the result C, some remnant of the calculation D also remaining, to give state (C,D). The input $(St,a1,O)$ causes the arithmetic unit to store the result of the computation in location $a1$ of the store; i.e., the state (C,D) remains unchanged, while the unit outputs $(a1,C,O)$ to the store. Again, it is clear that this unit is a finite automaton—it has a specified response for each of its finite number of input-state pairs.

The input to the logic unit (Fig. 1.6) is simply an instruction from the store. Input $Opabc$ causes it to change state to (Op,a,b,c). If Op is the name of a function, the logic unit then emits four outputs, one after another, in the following order: $(a,O,a1)$ and then $(b,O,a2)$ to store, thus placing the operands; (Op,O,O) to the arithmetic unit, thus causing the operation to be carried out;

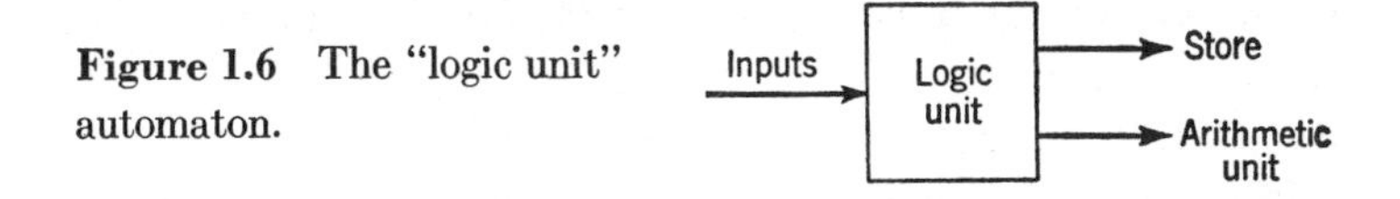

Figure 1.6 The "logic unit" automaton.

and, fourth, (c,O,l) to the store, causing it to prime the logic unit with the next instruction.

If Op is the store operation St, then it has two outputs: (St,a,O) to the arithmetic unit and then (c,O,l) to the store.

If Op is a branch operation Br (so that $Brabc$ means test word at address a; if the answer is "yes," next instruction is at b; if "no," it is at c), one can devise the logic unit to carry out the test in a finite way and accordingly emit (b,O,l) or (c,O,l) to the store. Anyway, the logic unit is a finite automaton. These details suffice for our construction of a computer. I leave the construction of an *input/output* finite automaton (and the construction of corresponding inputs for the logic unit) as an exercise for the reader.

Those readers who have had any experience with computers will know that a digital computer is made up of a network of tens of thousands of elements such as magnetic-core memory elements, flip-flops, or transistors and in this light it is of course obvious that a computer is a modular net, even though the modules are not strictly our McCulloch-Pitts neurons. To the novice, however, the above breakdown should provide some useful insight beyond the mere knowledge that a computer is a collection of electronic components. We note that different computers have different logical organizations, so that the scheme we have discussed embodies general ideas rather than the particular circuitry of any actual machine. We conclude this section with two references. A slim, readable volume is John von Neumann's "The Computer and the Brain."† A massive technical reference is "Computers and Data Processing," edited by Grabbe, Ramo, and Wooldridge.‡

† Yale University Press, New Haven, Conn., 1958.

‡ "Handbook of Automation, Computation, and Control," vol. 2, John Wiley & Sons, Inc., New York, 1958–1961.

1.5 Turing Machines

A computer thus emerges as a finite automaton or modular network which has command over its input and output—it can postpone its input, refer back to earlier inputs, etc. What we have essentially shown, then, is that any computation which we may carry out on a digital computer (using a finite repertoire of instructions) may be carried out by a Turing machine, where:

Definition 1.5.1 A *Turing machine* Z is a finite automaton A, together with a potentially infinite tape (which at any moment contains only a finite number of nonblank symbols) divided lengthwise into squares (each square being blank or bearing one symbol) and a device D for scanning one square of the tape at a time, printing a new symbol on the scanned square, and moving the tape one square to the left or one square to the right. The tape symbols belong to a finite alphabet I. (For convenience, we assume that I includes the blank or empty square.)

The input to A at any time is the symbol from I scanned by D. The output of A, determined by this symbol from I and A's internal state, is a member of $(I \times M) \cup (\text{stop})$† where $M = \{L,R,N\}$. If it is "stop," then Z stops computing. If it is (i,m), then the automaton A causes the device D to print i on the square it scans and then to move the tape one square to the Left, one square to the Right, or No squares at all, depending on whether m is L, R, or N.

Definition 1.5.2 *We associate a function* F_Z *with a Turing machine* Z by defining $F_Z(n_1,n_2, \ldots, n_r)$ to be the number of ones on the tape when Z stops, if started in the initial state q_0, say, scanning the leftmost of the string

$$\underbrace{1 \ldots 1}_{n_1+1} \text{ blank } \underbrace{1 \ldots 1}_{n_2+1} \text{ blank } \ldots \text{ blank } \underbrace{1 \ldots 1}_{n_r+1}$$

[denoted $\overline{(n_1, n_2, \ldots, n_r)}$] on an otherwise blank tape; if Z never stops after being so started, F_Z is to be undefined.

† Recall (cf. Appendix) that $\cup$ denotes the set-theoretic union.

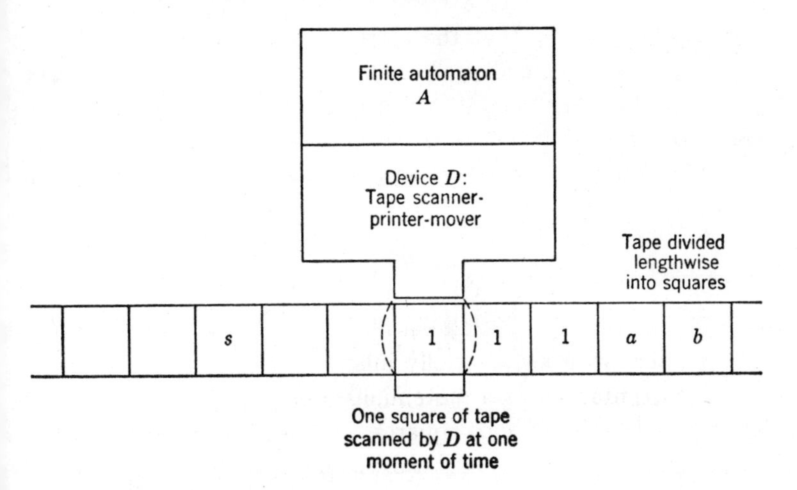

Figure 1.7 A Turing machine.

The reader should note that in the above definition we have assumed that our machine treats a blank square of tape as if it actually bore a special symbol, the "blank" symbol.

We give a special name to the functions F_Z of one variable:

Definition 1.5.3 A function f on the natural numbers† is called *partial recursive* if

$$f(n) = F_Z(n)$$

for some Turing machine Z, and all natural numbers n (where the equality implies that if one side is undefined, then both sides are).

A partial recursive function is called *recursive* if it is defined for all n.

Definition 1.5.2 involves a number of arbitrary conventions. The power of the definition is that the collection of all F_Z's, as Z ranges over the collection of all Turing machines, does not depend upon these conventions.‡ In particular, then, we feel

† We here mean by the natural numbers the set $N = \{0,1,2,3, \ldots\}$.

‡ We make no attempt to prove this here. For a discussion see, e.g., "Computability and Unsolvability," by Martin Davis.

justified in believing that the class of all partial recursive functions naturally embodies formally (i.e., mathematically) the intuitive idea of a function which can be computed by a digital computer.

Example: We construct a Turing machine (+) for which

$$F_{(+)}(n_1,n_2) = n_1 + n_2$$

Starting with the string $\overline{(n_1,n_2)}$, (+) has to produce a string containing only $n_1 + n_2$ ones. This is, of course, very easy. We may easily see (+) is given by the automaton

$$(\{1, \text{blank}\}, ((\text{blank}) \times M) \cup (\text{stop}), \{q_0,q_1,q_2\},\lambda,\delta)$$

with

$$\lambda(q_0,1) = q_1 \qquad \delta(q_0,1) = (\text{blank}, R)$$
$$\lambda(q_1, \text{blank}) = q_1 \qquad \delta(q_1, \text{blank}) = (\text{blank}, R)$$
$$\lambda(q_1,1) = q_2 \qquad \delta(q_1,1) = (\text{blank}, R)$$
$$\delta(q_2,1) = \delta(q_2, \text{blank}) = \text{stop}$$

all else defined arbitrarily.

The reader may follow the operation of the Turing machine (+) in the lists below (the state is written to the left of the symbol scanned by the machine at the given time):

$n_1 = 0$	$n_1 > 0$
$q_0 1 b\, 1 \ldots$	$q_0 1\, 1 \ldots$
$b q_1 b\, 1 \ldots$	$b q_1\, 1 \ldots$
$b b q_1\, 1\ \ldots$	$b b q_2 \ldots$
$b b b q_2 \ldots$	STOP
STOP	

That is, (+) merely removes the first two ones from its initial string.†

If we refer back to our Definition 1.5.1 of a Turing machine, we see that all the information we need about its structure is contained in the structure of its constituent finite automaton

$$A = (I,(I \times M) \cup (\text{stop}),S,\lambda,\delta)$$

† More sophisticated examples are given in chap. 1 of Davis's book.

Since I and S are finite sets, we may easily enumerate their elements

$$I = \{i_1, i_2, \ldots, i_m\} \qquad S = \{s_1, s_2, \ldots, s_n\}$$

We may now represent A by a list of quintuples

$$s_k i_l i_n m s_p \tag{1.5.1}$$

where there is one quintuple for all pairs (s_k, i_l) such that $\delta(s_k, i_l) \neq$ stop and where

$$(i_n, m) = \delta(s_k, i_l) \qquad s_p = \lambda(s_k, i_l)$$

Clearly, there is a one-one correspondence between such lists and finite automata of our desired form. Now the possible values of k, l, n, and p are all enumerable,† and there are three possible values of m. Hence the collection of all quintuples (1.5.1) is enumerable. Hence the collection of all finite lists of such quintuples is enumerable. Hence the collection of all our automata is enumerable.

Further, we may enumerate our automata in an effective way‡ so that, given an integer n, it is possible to give our nth automaton. We may define the *weight* of the quintuple (1.5.1) to be the natural number $k + l + n + m + p$ (on setting $L = 1$, $R = 2$, $N = 3$). Then there are only a finite number of automata defined by a list of at most n quintuples, each of weight at most n, and these lists we may arrange in a conventional lexicographic order. Call these automata of degree n. Then we get an effective enumeration (with repetitions, but this does not matter) by writing down the automata of degree 1, then those of degree 2, then those of degree 3, ad infinitum, the automata of each degree being arranged in lexicographic order. Hence:

Theorem 1.5.1 The collection of all Turing machines is effectively enumerable:

† Recall that a collection is enumerable if we may arrange its members in numerical order: first, second, third, etc.

‡ We shall elucidate the sense in which we use "effective" in Sec. 1.6.

$Z_1, Z_2, Z_3, \ldots$

We immediately have, then,

Corollary 1.5.2 The collection of all recursively enumerable sets is effectively enumerable:

$S_1, S_2, S_3, \ldots$

where

Definition 1.5.4 A set S is *recursively enumerable* if $S = \{f(n) \mid n \varepsilon N\}$, for some partial recursive function f.

We conclude this section with one more definition, which we will need in the next section.

Definition 1.5.5 A set S is *recursive* if its characteristic function† is a recursive function.

1.6 Turing's Hypothesis and Recursive Sets

In this section, I want to derive some results in the theory of recursive functions. In Secs. 5.3 through 5.5, we will use these results to prove Gödel's theorem: first, because it is an important theorem which few people realize has a proof accessible to the nonspecialist; and second, because a clear view of its proof will enable us to discuss its implications for the relative power of brains and machines.

Let me crystallize the idea of an *effective procedure*. There are certain computations for which there exist mechanical rules, or *algorithms*—e.g., the Euclidean algorithm for finding the greatest common divisor of two integers. Certainly, any computation which can be carried out by an electronic computer is governed by purely mechanical rules. We say, then, that there exists an effective pro-

† The characteristic function $C_S(n)$ of S is 0 if n is not in S, and 1 if n is in S.

cedure for carrying out these computations. There are many cases in which we do not really know how to write a program which could cause a given computer to carry out the desired computation, but we do have a strong intuitive feeling that an effective procedure exists for that computation. On the other hand, we do not feel that there is an effective procedure for *predicting* the outcome of a coin toss, for example.

Now, we saw in Sec. 1.5 that any process which can be carried out by a digital computer can also be carried out by a Turing machine. In view of the great generality of the processes we allowed our hypothetical computer of Sec. 1.4, we are tempted to make the following hypothesis, following Turing in his original 1936 paper: *Turing's hypothesis: The informal intuitive notion of an effective procedure on sequences of symbols is identical with our precise concept of one which may be executed by a Turing machine.*

Such a hypothesis can never be given a formal proof, simply because a formal proof requires definitions of the concepts involved —and such a formal definition is incompatible with the idea of an intuitive concept! All one can adduce is a "proof" by inductive inference: To date, wherever in the development of the theory of recursive functions it has been intuitively evident that an effective procedure exists, it has always been possible to devise a Turing machine to execute a rigorous analog of the process.

My presentation in this section, then, will be rigorous save for one reservation: If it is intuitively evident that a procedure is effective, I shall take it as proven that a suitable Turing machine exists. You may rest assured that in every case a rigorous proof exists—I refer you to "Computability and Unsolvability" by Martin Davis.

Let me first recouch our definitions in our intuitive language of effective procedures:

Definition 1.6.1 A *function* is called *recursive* if there exists an effective procedure for computing it.

Definition 1.6.2 A *set* is *recursive* if there exists an effective procedure for telling whether or not an element belongs to it.

Definition 1.6.3 A *set* is *recursively enumerable* if there exists an effective procedure for generating its elements, one after another.

Example: The set of squares of integers is recursively enumerable—we take 1, 2, 3, . . . in turn and square them. It is also recursive—given any integer we decompose it into its prime factors and then tell easily whether or not it is square. We shall see that every recursive set is recursively enumerable, but that the converse is not true. The latter result is relatively deep. We now have two sets of definitions, formal and informal. If a function is recursive in the formal sense, it is certainly recursive in the informal sense—our effective procedure is simply to compute the function with the Turing machine given to us by the formal definition. Similarly, a set which is recursive (or recursively enumerable) in the formal sense must be recursive (or recursively enumerable) in the informal sense. It is the converse statement (e.g., that if a set is recursive in the informal sense of Definition 1.6.2, then it is recursive in the formal sense of Definition 1.5.5) which constitutes, for us, Turing's hypothesis. If I want to convince a computer user that a program exists for making a computation—without consideration for time or storage limitations—then I show him the flow diagrams for making a computation, not the program in machine language. The proofs I give, then, are related to the rigorous proofs as the flow diagram is related to the machine-language program. I hope to show all the essentials, merely omitting those finicky details which serve only to obscure initial understanding. We now prove theorems on recursive and recursively enumerable sets.

Theorem 1.6.1 If R and S are recursively enumerable sets, then so are $R \cup S$ and $R \cap S$.†

Proof If we have effective procedures P_R and P_S for generating R and S, we need merely use them "simultaneously" to obtain an effective procedure for generating $R \cup S$.

† See Appendix.

Now P_R generates R element by element, so that we obtain from it m_1, then m_2, then m_3, etc., where the m_i are all the elements belonging to R. Similarly, P_S yields n_1, n_2, n_3, etc., belonging to S. Our effective procedure for generating $R \cap S$ is then as follows:

Use P_R and P_S alternately to produce m_1, then n_1, m_2, then n_2, m_3, then n_3, etc. As each m_i is produced, we see if it equals an n_j already generated. If it does, we emit it as an element of $R \cap S$. If not, we proceed to generate n_i and apply a similar test to it. In this way, we effectively produce all elements of $R \cap S$. Q.E.D.

Theorem 1.6.2 A set S of positive integers is recursive if and only if both S and $\overline{S}$ are recursively enumerable.†

Proof If S is recursive, we generate 0, 1, 2, 3, . . . in their natural order and, as an integer is generated, we test if it is in S; if it is, we emit it as belonging to S. Thus an effective process is set up for generating the elements of S, so that S is recursively enumerable. Likewise, $\overline{S}$ is recursively enumerable.

Conversely, let both S and $\overline{S}$ be recursively enumerable, and let $n_1, n_2, n_3, \ldots$ be a recursive enumeration of S; $m_1, m_2, m_3, \ldots$ of $\overline{S}$. Given a natural number n, generate in order $n_1, m_1, n_2, m_2, n_3, m_3, \ldots$, and so on, comparing each with n. Since n must be in either S or $\overline{S}$, we shall thus eventually come across an n_i or m_j identical with n and accordingly discover n to be in S or $\overline{S}$. Hence, an effective method is set up for determining of any natural number whether or not it is in S. Hence S is recursive. Q.E.D.

Before turning to our next theorem, we remind the reader that there exists an effective enumeration of the ordered pairs of natural numbers, called the *diagonal method*. It is shown in Fig. 1.8.

The pair (x,y) appears in the xth row and yth column. We proceed by passing up successive diagonals starting from the top left-hand corner. The first few pairs in this enumeration are

† See Appendix.

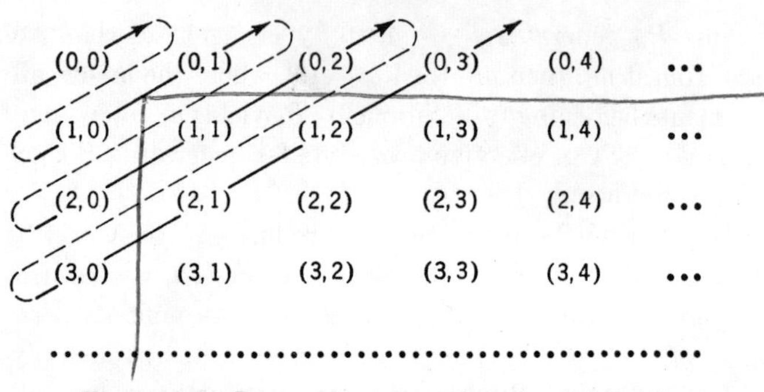

Figure 1.8 Diagonal enumeration of ordered pairs.

(0,0), (1,0), (0,1), (2,0), (1,1), (0,2), (3,0), (2,1), ... The reader may verify that the pair (x,y) falls in the $\frac{1}{2}(x^2 + 2xy + y^2 + 3y + x + 2)$th place in this sequence.

Theorem 1.6.3 There exists a recursively enumerable set of positive integers which is not recursive.

Proof By Theorem 1.6.2, this is equivalent to the existence of a recursively enumerable set of natural numbers whose complement is *not* recursively enumerable.

Now let $S_1, S_2, \ldots$ be our effective enumeration of the recursively enumerable sets (cf. Corollary 1.5.2). At step $\tau(x,y)$ [where (x,y) is the $\tau(x,y)$th pair in some effective enumeration of pairs of natural numbers—e.g., the diagonal method] generate the xth element of S_y; and whenever y is thus generated in S_y, place y in a set U. U is thus recursively enumerable. y is in U if and only if y is in S_y. Hence, y is in $\overline{U}$ if and only if y is not in S_y. We thus see that $\overline{U}$ differs from every recursively enumerable set in the presence or absence of at least one integer. Thus $\overline{U}$ is not recursively enumerable, and hence U is not recursive. Q.E.D.

This theorem really constitutes an abstract form of Gödel's theorem. The hard work of Secs. 5.3 through 5.5 will be to define and understand Gödel's concepts so that we may discern his theorem in the very general statement of Theorem 1.6.3.

We cannot leave the topic of Turing machines without mentioning universal Turing machines—i.e., Turing machines that can carry out the computation of *any* Turing machine. To make this idea precise, let us recall Theorem 1.5.1 and associate a Turing machine Z with the number n, where Z_n is the first occurrence of Z in the effective enumeration

$$Z_1, Z_2, Z_3, \ldots$$

of the Turing machines. We can now state precisely the existence of a universal Turing machine (cf. Definition 1.5.2):

Theorem 1.6.4 There exists a universal Turing machine U such that

$$F_{Z_n}(x) = F_U(n,x)$$

for all Turing machines Z_n and all integers x.

Proof Given n and x, we can find Z_n effectively and then use it to compute $F_{Z_n}(x)$ effectively. Thus F_U is effectively computable, and so Turing's hypothesis tells us that the required U exists. Q.E.D.

The reader who feels cheated by the above use of Turing's hypothesis may refer to Turing's 1936 paper for an explicit construction of a universal Turing machine. (But look out for a few small errors in the construction.)

1.7 Regular and Realizable Events

The "life" of a finite automaton progresses by discrete moments $t = 1, 2, 3, \ldots$, and "his view of the world" derives entirely from the sequence of inputs "he" receives during these moments. Hence, if at any time we ask "him" whether an event has occurred (we agree to interpret some of the output symbols as a "yes," all others as a "no"), "his reply" can only depend on the input sequence. The only type of event, then, that can possibly enter into the "life" of an automaton is a collection of input sequences. We thus decree, for the purposes of our work in this section, that:

Definition 1.7.1 An *event* is a subset of the set of all input sequences from some finite alphabet.

If a_1, a_2, a_3, a_4, say, are inputs of the automaton, we shall make the convention that $a_1a_2a_3a_4$ is the input sequence in which a_1 comes first, a_2 second, etc.

We can then make a trivial model of perception of an event by saying that an event E is "perceptible" (or "realizable") by a finite automaton A if A can say "yes" to the event. More formally:

Definition 1.7.2 *An event E is realizable* if there exists a finite automaton $A = (I,O,S,\lambda,\delta)$, a splitting of O into two disjoint sets YES and NO, and a designated initial state s_0 such that an input sequence $a_1 \ldots a_n$ belongs to E if and only if when A is started in state s_0 and receives inputs $a_1, a_2, \ldots, a_n$ in succession, it finally emits a YES output.

Let 1 be an input of A. Then, no matter what A may be, the event $E = \{1 \ldots 1(n \text{ times}) \mid n \text{ is a square}\}$ is not realizable; i.e., there are nonrealizable events. We shall prove and discuss this fact at the end of the section. Our task now is to give a precise characterization of the realizable events. The reader may choose to omit the *proofs* of Lemmas 1.7.1 and 1.7.2 without greatly impairing his understanding of this characterization.

Certainly *the empty event and the events consisting of a single input sequence of length one are realizable.*

We define three operations on events:

Definition 1.7.3 If E and F are two events (i.e., sets of sequences) then we define:

$E \cup F$ (E union F) $\quad$ $x \in E \cup F$ if and only if $x \in E$ or $x \in F$

$E \cdot F$ (E dot F)	$x \varepsilon E \cdot F$ if and only if the sequence x can be written in the form ef; i.e., a sequence e of E followed by a sequence f of F
E^* (E star)	$x \varepsilon E^*$ if and only if the sequence x can be written in the form $e_1 \ldots e_n$ for some n, and sequences $e_1, \ldots, e_n$ from E.

If we define $E^1 = E$, $E^{n+1} = E^n \cdot E$, then we see that $E^* = E \cup E^2 \cup E^3 \cup E^4 \cup \ldots.$

Lemma 1.7.1 If E and F are realizable events, then so are $E \cup F$, $E \cdot F$, and F^*.

Proof Let $A(E) = (I,O,S,\lambda,\delta)$ realize E and $A(F) = (I',O',S',\lambda',\delta')$ realize F, with initial states s_0, s_0', respectively. Without loss of generality, we may assume $I = I'$; and $O = O' = \{yes, no\}$ (i.e., we lump all the outputs of each class together to form one output).

Our lemma is proved by the following constructions:

a. $A(E \cup F) = (I,O,S \times S',\lambda \times \lambda',\delta'')$ where the initial state is (s_0,s_0');

$$(\lambda \times \lambda')((s,s'),i) = (\lambda(s,i),\lambda'(s',i))$$

and

$\delta''((s,s'),i) = yes$ if and only if $\delta(s,i) = yes$ or $\delta'(s',i) = yes$

b. This construction is more sophisticated. Let $2^{S'}$ denote the set of all subsets of S'. Then

$$A(E \cdot F) = (I,O,S \times 2^{S'},\bar{\lambda},\tilde{\delta})$$

where the initial state is $(s_0,\emptyset)$†;

† $\emptyset$ is the empty set. Thus $\emptyset$ is a subset of S', and $so \emptyset \varepsilon 2^{S'}$, cf. Appendix.

$\bar{\lambda}((s,T),i) = (\lambda(s,i), \{\lambda'(t,i) \mid t \in T\} \cup R)$

where $R = \emptyset$ if $\delta(s,i) = no$

$R = \{s_0'\}$ if $\delta(s,i) = yes$

$\bar{\delta}((s,T),i) = yes$ if and only if $\delta'(t,i) = yes$ for some $t \in T$

c. $A(F^*) = (I,O,2^{S'},\bar{\lambda},\bar{\delta})$

where the initial state is $\{s_0'\}$

$\bar{\lambda}(T,i) = \{\lambda'(t,i) \mid t \in T\} \cup R$

where $R = \{s_0'\}$ if and only if $\delta'(t,i) = yes$ for some $t \in T$, otherwise $R = \emptyset$

$\delta(T,i) = yes$ if and only if $\delta'(t,i) = yes$ for some $t \in T$.

Q.E.F.

What we have just proved is that all regular events are realizable, where:

Definition 1.7.4 A set E of sequences is *regular* if

a. E is empty or contains precisely one member, or

b. E can be obtained from the empty set and the one-member sets by a finite number of applications of the union, dot, and star operations of Definition 1.7.3

We now show that all realizable events are regular; i.e., the regular events provide our desired precise characterization of the realizable events. To this end we need a lemma.

Lemma 1.7.2 Let T be a finite set and let R be a binary operation on T (i.e., for each pair a, b from T, either "aRb", "a is in the relation R to b", or "not aRb"). A sequence $a_1, \ldots, a_m$ of elements of T is called an *R-transition sequence* if and only if a_iRa_{i+1} for $i = 1, \ldots, m - 1$. Then, for any two members a and b of T, the set of all R-transition sequences from a to b is regular.

Proof By induction on n, the number of symbols in T.

a. $n = 1 \qquad T = \{a\}$

If aRa, then our set of sequences is $\{a,aa,aaa, \ldots\} = \{a\}^*$ and so is regular. If not aRa, our set is simply $\{a\}$, which is again regular.

b. $n > 1$. We assume the theorem proved for smaller values. Any R-transition sequence from a to b can be written

$$aA_1aA_2a \ldots aA_maBb \tag{1.7.1}$$

where the sequences A_i and B contain no occurrence of a. Let

$$C = \{x \mid aRx\} \qquad D = \{x \mid xRa\} \qquad E = \{x \mid xRb\}$$

Then each A_i is a transition sequence from a member of C to a member of D, and B is a transition sequence from a member of C to a member of E. Let R_{xy} be the set of R-transition sequences from x to y—by induction hypothesis, it is regular (on alphabet $T - \{a\}$, with $n - 1$ members) for $x \in C$, $y \in D$, or $x \in C$, $y \in E$.

Since union preserves regularity, then

$$\bigcup\{R_{xy} \mid x \in C, y \in D\} = F$$

and

$$\bigcup\{R_{xy} \mid x \in C, y \in E\} = G$$

are regular. But now inspection of (1.7.1) shows that

$$R_{ab} = (\{a\} \cdot F)^* \cdot (\{a\} \cdot G \cdot \{b\})$$

so that R_{ab} is regular. Q.E.D.

Now let us return to the event E and the finite automaton A of Definition 1.7.2 which realizes it. We take for our T of the lemma the set $S \times I$ of state-input pairs. We define our binary relation by $(c,d)\, R(e,f)$ if and only if $e = \lambda(c,d)$, i.e., (c,d) sends our automaton A into state e. An input sequence $a_0 \ldots a_m$ belongs to E

if and only if $(s_0,a_0),(s_1,a_1), \ldots, (s_m,a_m)$ is an R-transition sequence with $\delta(s_m,a_m) \varepsilon YES$. Hence, if E' is the union

$$\bigcup \{R_{(s_0,a_0)(s_m,a_m)} \mid a_0 \varepsilon I, \delta(s_m,a_m) \varepsilon YES\}$$

it is regular. But E is obtained from E' by extracting second members from the pairs. Referring back to Definitions 1.7.3 and 1.7.4, we see that this operation does not destroy regularity, i.e., we have proved:

Theorem 1.7.1 An event is realizable if and only if it is regular.

The advantage of this theorem is that it allows us to express mathematically those things which a fixed-structure, finite deterministic automaton can do. The language of regular events has become a standard tool of thinking for engineers engaged in switching theory—the design of such automata as networks of switching relays and similar components.

Now, to validate our claim made at the start of this section that the event

$$S = \{1 \ldots 1 \text{ (n times)} \mid n \text{ is a square}\} \tag{1.7.2}$$

is not realizable by *any* automaton A, we need only convince ourselves that it is not a regular event. Let P_k be the property of any event E that there exist k consecutive numbers $m = n, \ldots, n + k - 1$ for which $1 \ldots 1$ (m times) does not belong to E, while $1 \ldots 1$ ($n + k$ times) belongs to E. Then our event S in (1.7.2) has the property P_k for all k. Using Definition 1.7.4, the reader may satisfy himself by induction that no event with the property P_k for all k can be regular. Hence "the set of squares" is *not regular.*

However, we know (cf. our example in Sec. 1.6) that the set of all squares is *recursive.* We thus see that Turing machines are more powerful than finite automata. Put another way, we see that by giving a finite automaton its own receptors and effectors by which it can to some extent *control* its environment (e.g., a tape scanner-printer-mover whereby it can manipulate its tape and hence act as a Turing machine) we can radically alter its possible range of behavior. We shall consider such alterations of behavior in greater generality when we discuss "feedback" in Sec. 4.1.

Bibliography: Chapter 1

A more detailed introductory account of neurophysiology for the layman is given in

1. Eccles, J. C.: The Physiology of the Imagination, *Sci. Am.*, **199** (3): 135–146 (1958).

For a technical account see, e.g.,

2. Ranson, S. W., and S. L. Clark: "The Anatomy of the Nervous System," 10th ed., W. B. Saunders Company, Philadelphia and London, 1959.

The McCulloch-Pitts model was first propounded in

3. McCulloch, W. S., and Pitts, W.: A Logical Calculus of the Ideas Immanent in Nervous Activity, *Bull. Math. Biophys.*, **5**: 115–133 (1943). The reader is warned that Part 3 is incomprehensible!

A superb paper on finite automata (though restricted to a "yes" or "no" output) is

4. Rabin, M. O., and Scott, D.: Finite Automata and Their Decision Problems, *IBM J. Res. Develop.*, **3**: 114–125 (1959).

The concept of regular event first appears in

5. Kleene, S. C.: Representation of Events in Nerve Nets and Finite Automata, in C. E. Shannon and J. McCarthy (eds.), "Automata Studies," Princeton University Press, Princeton, N.J., 1956, pp. 3–42.

Kleene's main result receives a more polished treatment in

6. Copi, I. M., Elgot, C. C., and Wright, J. B.: Realisation of Events by Logical Nets, *J. Assoc. Computing Mach.*, **5**: 181–196 (1958).

Our approach in Sec. 1.7 in turn polishes the above treatment. Some of our material appeared in less polished form in

7. Arbib, Michael: Turing Machines, Finite Automata and Neural Nets, *J. Assoc. Computing Mach.*, **8**: 467–475 (1961).

Turing machines are named after Turing who defined them in his paper

8. Turing, A. M.: On Computable Numbers with an Application to the Entscheidungsproblem, *Proc. London Math. Soc.*, ser. 2, **42**: 230–265 (1936). See also correction in **43**: 544–546 (1936–37).

A text on Turing machines and their use in the theory of recursive functions is

9. Davis, Martin: "Computability and Unsolvability," McGraw-Hill Book Company, Inc., New York, 1958.

The clear, informal proofs of Theorems 1.6.2 and 1.6.3 are akin to those in the really superb paper (which I recommend to your attention)

10. Post, Emil L.: Recursively Enumerable Sets and Their Decision Problems, *Bull. Am. Math. Soc.*, **50**: 284–316 (1944).

The reader who wishes to sample "wire and transistor" neural modeling at a very high level of sophistication should read

11. Harmon, Leon D.: Studies with Artificial Neurons, *Kybernetik*, **1** (3): 89–101 (1961).

Collateral reading for the present volume will be found in the recently published

12. Wooldridge, Dean E.: "The Machinery of the Brain," McGraw-Hill Book Company, Inc., New York, 1963.

2

Structure and Randomness

2.1 The Visual System of the Frog

In this section we are going to discuss a particular example of *structure* in the brain. To this end, we shall look at the work of Lettvin, Maturana, McCulloch, and Pitts reported in the following papers: "What the Frog's Eye Tells the Frog's Brain," *Proc.* IRE, **47**: 1940–1951 (1959); "Physiology and Anatomy of Vision in the Frog," *J. Gen. Physiol.* **43** (Suppl.): 129–175 (1960); "Two Remarks on the Visual System of the Frog," in W. Rosenblith (ed.), "Sensory Communication," The M.I.T. Press, Cambridge, Mass., pp. 757–776, 1961. Following their lead, we shall study the structure of the frog's visual system.

Frogs feed on insects which they detect solely by vision. They prey only on moving insects, and their attention is never attracted by stationary objects. A large moving object provokes an escape reaction. For them, a form deprived of movement seems to be behaviorally meaningless. They seem to recognize their prey and

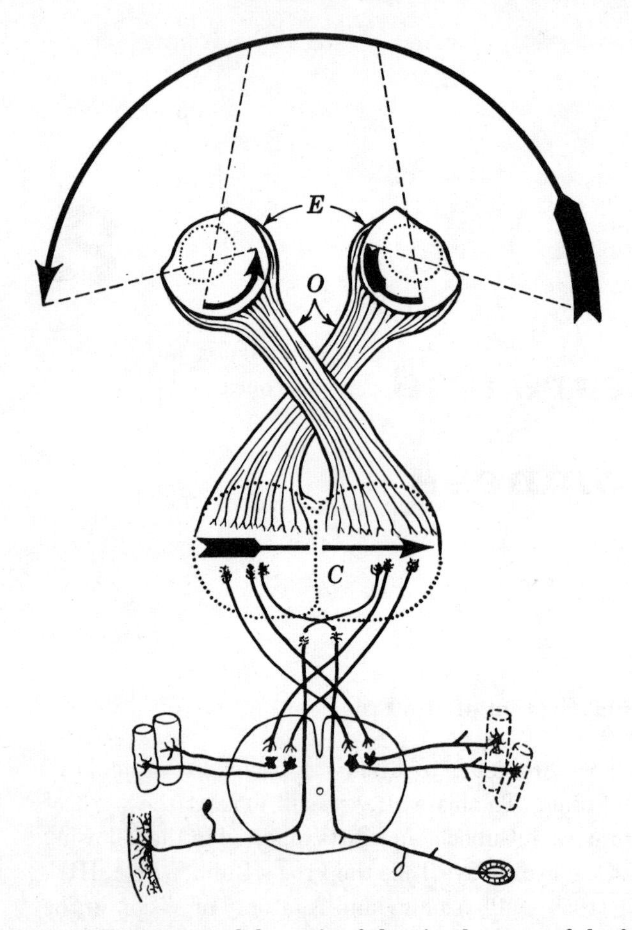

Figure 2.1 Schematic of the visual system of the frog.

select it for attack from among all other environmental objects because it exhibits a number of features such as movement, a certain size, some contrast, and perhaps also a certain color. This ability of frogs to recognize their prey and snap at it is not altered by changes in the general environment, e.g., changes in illumination.

Lettvin et al. addressed themselves to an investigation of the frog visual system designed to locate those properties of the system, if any, which assist the frog in recognizing the universals† *prey* and *enemy*.

Figure 2.1 shows the two eyes *E* of the frog, the optic nerves *O* proceeding back and crossing over, and the first portion of the brain they reach *C*, which is called the *superior colliculus* or *optic tectum*. (Other portions of the brain shown will not enter the present discussion.) The arrows give some idea of how the visual stimulus is mapped back to the colliculus.

Light enters the eye and passes to the back, where it enters the retina, passes through the transparent ganglion and internuncial cells, and finally reaches the rods and cones.

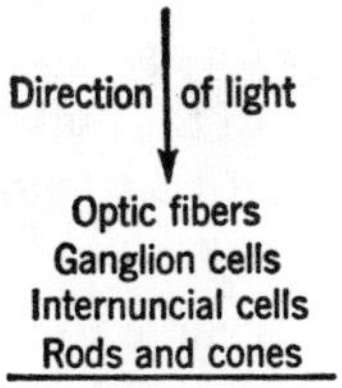

Figure 2.2 Passage of light through the frog retina.

When sufficiently stimulated by light, the rods and cones produce generator potentials (continuously variable *dc* potentials) which in turn, via the above internuncial neurons, elicit impulses. The axons of these internuncial cells, in turn, impinge on the dendritic trees of the ganglion cells (neurons). The optic fibers are the axons of the ganglions—these fibers pass across the retina and come together at the blind spot, where they pass through the retina in a bundle called the optic nerve, which passes back to the brain.

The frog has about 1 million receptors (i.e., rods and cones), 2½ to 3½ million internuncial neurons, and ½ million ganglion cells. Such numbers make it seem unlikely that the complex structure of the retina merely acts as a repeater that transmits

† The Oxford English Dictionary tells us that a "universal" is "what is predicated of all the individuals or species of a class or genus; an abstract or general concept regarded as having an absolute, mental, or nominal existence; a general term or notion."

intact to the brain the pattern of light and dark formed on the receptors. One is thus led to believe that the retina analyzes the visual image and transmits abstracted information to the visual centers.

In 1938 Hartline showed that the ganglion cells could be grouped in 3 classes, according to their response to a small spot of light on their receptive fields. (The *receptive field* of a ganglion cell is defined as the portion of the visual field mapped on the collection of all those receptors whose activity affects that of the given ganglion cell.) These classes were as follows:

a. *On* cells, which respond with a prolonged but delayed discharge to the *on* of the spot of light
b. *On-off* cells, which respond with small bursts of high frequency to the make and break (i.e., change of *off* to *on*, or of *on* to *off*) of that light
c. *Off* cells, which respond with a prolonged and immediate discharge to the *off* of that light

These observations were the first to show that the ganglion cells perform several complex operations on the visual image. But spots of light are not natural stimuli for the frog in the way that a fly or a worm is. Their use has suggested that the ganglions repeat to some extent, but in a coarser and inconstant manner, the original pattern of the visual image weighted by local differences. But the perception of universals that is obvious in the behavior of the frog seems to demand the presence of some functional invariants in the activity of the components of its visual system. That is, we expect that the retina might carry out computations on the visual image which serve to reveal crucial properties, such as the presence of a prey or an enemy. Lettvin et al. sought to find appropriate functional invariants, and hence the analytic functions of the ganglion cells, by adopting a naturalistic approach and studying them in terms of their response to real objects of the natural environment.

In their study they used the common American frog, *Rana pipiens.* The frog was placed so that one eye was in the center of

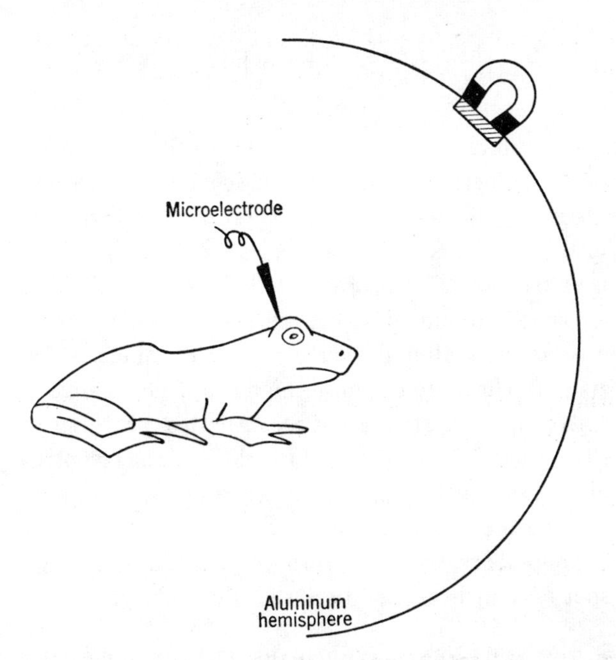

Figure 2.3 Setup for study of the frog visual system.

a hemisphere 14 inches in diameter, which formed the experimental visual field. An electrode was inserted into the frog so that it could respond either to the activity of a single ganglion cell (by placing the tip of the electrode on the axon of the cell in the optic nerve) or to that of a cell in the colliculi. The aluminum hemisphere represents about two-thirds of the visual field of one frog eye. By proper orientation of the animal, one could cover any desired part of the visual field and could entirely control the receptive field of the cells under study. The stimulating objects were moved on the inner surface by means of a magnet moved on the external surface. Numerous shapes and kinds of objects were used, e.g., dark disks, dark strips, and dark squares. (*Note that the stimuli thus did not bear on color response.*)†

† A recent paper dealing with color response is W. R. A. Muntz, Effectiveness of Different Colors of Light Releasing the Positive Photoactic Behavior of Frogs . . . , *J. Neurophysiol.*, **25**: 712–720 (1962).

It was found that the response of ganglion cells fell into five groups:

GROUP I. THE BOUNDARY DETECTORS. These fibers have receptive fields 2 to 4 degrees in diameter. They respond to any boundary between two shades of gray in the receptive field, provided it is sharp. Sharpness of boundary rather than degree of contrast seems to be what is measured. The response is enhanced if the boundary is moved and is unchanged if the illumination of the particular contrast is altered over a very wide range. If no boundary exists in the field, no response can be got from change of lighting, no matter how sharp the change. Another property of the group I cells is that if a boundary is brought into the receptive field in total darkness and the light is switched on, a continuing response occurs after a short initial delay.

Axons of group I are the "on" fibers of Hartline—a small, well-focused spot of light is defined by a sharp boundary.

GROUP II. THE MOVEMENT-GATED, DARK CONVEX BOUNDARY DETECTORS. These fibers have receptive fields of 3 to 5 degrees. They too respond only to sharp boundaries between two grays, but only if that boundary is curved, the darker area being convex, and if the boundary is moved or has moved. Again, the responses are invariant over a wide range of illumination, roughly that between dim twilight and bright noon. They do not belong to any of Hartline's classes—they do not respond to spots of light, stimuli whose lighter areas are convex, which are not moved.

GROUP III. THE MOVING OR CHANGING CONTRAST DETECTORS. These fibers have receptive fields 7 to 11 degrees in diameter. They are, in effect, Hartline's "on-off" fibers. However, they respond invariantly under wide changes of illumination to the same silhouette moved at the same speed across the same background. They have no enduring response, but fire only if the contrast is changing or moving. The response is better (higher in frequency) when the boundary is sharp or moving fast than when it is blurred or moving slowly.

GROUP IV. THE DIMMING DETECTORS. These detectors are Hartline's "off" fibers. They have a 15-degree receptive field. They respond to any dimming in the whole receptive field weighted by distance from the center of that field. Boundaries play no role in the response. The same percentage of dimming produces the same response, more or less independent of the level of lighting at the beginning.

GROUP V. This group is rare. We cannot even say whether it has a receptive field in the usual sense. It fires at a frequency that is inversely related to the intensity of the average illumination. When the lighting is changed, the frequency slowly changes to its new level.

Each ganglion cell belongs to only one of these groups, and the cells of each class are uniformly distributed across the retina. In any small retinal area, one finds representatives of all groups in proportion to their general relative frequencies.

The axons of the cells of each group end in a separate layer of the tectum. However, two of them are mixed (the terminals of group V end in the strata of terminals of group III), so that they really form four fundamental layers of terminals. Each of these four layers of terminals in the tectum forms a "continuous" map of the retina with respect to the operation performed by the corresponding ganglion cells. The four layers are in registration,† and at any point on a tectal lobe the terminals of all layers come from the same locus in the retina.

Thus the function of the retina of the frog is not to transmit information about the point-to-point pattern of distribution of light and dark in the image formed on it. On the contrary, it is mainly to analyze this image at every point in terms of four qualitative contexts (boundaries, moving curvatures, changing contrasts, and local dimming) and a measure of illumination and to send this information to the colliculi, where these functions are separated in the four congruent layers† of terminals.

† Points in different layers which are stacked atop each other correspond to the same small region of the retina.

The retina transforms the visual image from a mosaic of luminous points to a system of overlapping qualitative contexts in which any point is described in terms of how it is related to what is around it. Since the transformation of the image constitutes the fundamental function of the retina, it is then the integrative capability of the ganglion cells that is significant. These considerations led Lettvin and his colleagues to an anatomical inquiry into the capacity of the ganglion cells to combine the information impinging upon them, seeking a correlation between the different morphological types of ganglion cells (types differing in the structure of their dendritic trees) and the operations that they perform. It is to their efforts in this inquiry that we now turn.

There are five anatomically distinct ganglion cells, as shown in Fig. 2.4.

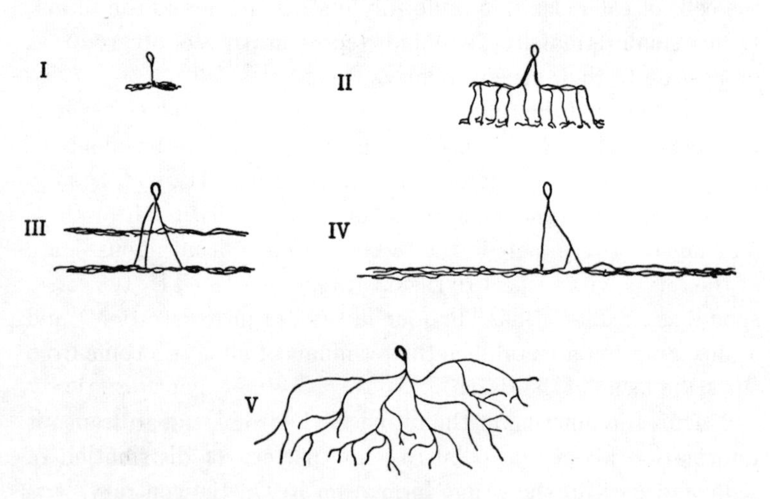

Figure 2.4 Five types of ganglion dendritic trees.

You will notice that the dendritic arrangements shown in the figure suggest that there are two major subdivisions of the inner plexiform layer,† although undoubtedly each subdivision can

† The layer of the retina occupied by the dendrites of the ganglions is called the *inner plexiform layer*.

be divided into several layers. For a discussion of the possible import of this fact, we refer the reader to the third of the original papers mentioned in the beginning of this section.

I. ONE-LEVEL CONSTRICTED FIELD: These are the smallest of the ganglion cells. The major dendrites extend only to the inner levels of the inner plexiform layer and there spread out in dense and constricted planar bush.

II. MANY-LEVEL *E* DISTRIBUTION: These are the next-to-smallest ganglion cells. The major dendrites extend only to the inner levels of the inner plexiform layer and there branch out in planar fashion. However, each branch emits twigs all along its course, and some extend into the outer levels of the inner plexiform layer, whereas others remain in the inner levels.

III. MANY-LEVEL *H* DISTRIBUTION: These are the next-to-largest ganglion cells. The major dendrites extend to the outer levels of the inner plexiform layer. However, they emit two widely spread arbors, one in the inner levels and one in the outer levels.

IV. ONE-LEVEL BROAD FIELD: These are the largest of the ganglion cells. The major dendrites extend to the outer levels of the inner plexiform layer and there branch widely over a considerable area.

V. DIFFUSE TREES: There are several sizes of these cells. The dendrites branch helter-skelter all over the inner plexiform layer and show no planar arrangement such as occurs in the other four kinds of cell.

If we should assume that the size of the dendritic field to some extent determines the size of the receptive field, we would emerge with a fairly definite correspondence between cell types and operations:

I. One-level constricted field	Boundary detection
II. Many-level E-shaped field	Movement-gated, dark convex boundary detectors

III. Many-level H-shaped field	Moving or changing contrast detectors
IV. One-level constricted field	Dimming detectors

More or less by default, we associate the diffuse type, which is rare, with the average light-level measuring group.

The above identifications are strengthened by these facts: The diameters of the dendritic fields match well the angular diameters of the receptive fields; the cell bodies are distributed in size in the same way as the dendritic fields; and if the axon diameters reflect soma size, then the largest axons ought to have the largest receptive fields and the smallest axons the smallest fields, and this seems to be the case. Further, receptive fields often appear to be not circular, but elliptical or cardioid. In Maturana's pictures of the ganglion cells, both elliptical and cardioid dendritic fields appear.

Turning from the ganglion cells to cells of the tectum, Lettvin and his colleagues found several kinds of cells. They were not able to define the subgroups at all well, but there are two major populations which they have named "newness neurons" and "sameness neurons." The former is concerned, it seems, with detection of novelty and visual events; the latter with continuity in time of interesting objects in the field of vision.

2.1.1 Comparisons

Embryology reveals that the retina is essentially a part of the brain. The work of Lettvin, Maturana, McCulloch, and Pitts, then, has laid bare some fundamental structure of the frog brain. It must, of course, be emphasized that their work applies only to the frog—neither the anatomy nor the receptive field operations are *necessarily* the same in mammals or even in other amphibia. Similar work on the cat's visual system has been done by D. H. Hubel and T. N. Wiesel.† They found, in the cat's visual cortex,

† Receptive Fields, Binocular Interaction, and Functional Architecture in the Cat's Visual Cortex, *J. Physiol.*, **160:** 106–154 (1962).

cells comparable to those which Lettvin et al. found in the colliculus of the frog. They comment:

> At first glance, it may seem astonishing that the complexity of third-order neurones in the frog's visual system should be equalled only by that of sixth-order neurones in the geniculo-cortical pathway of the cat. Yet this is less surprising if one notes the great anatomical differences in the two animals, especially the lack, in the frog, of any cortex or dorsal lateral geniculate body. There is undoubtedly a parallel difference in the use each animal makes of its visual system: the frog's visual apparatus is presumably specialised to recognise a limited number of stereotyped patterns or situations, compared with the high acuity and versatility found in the cat. Probably it is not so unreasonable to find that in the cat the specialization of cells for complex operations is postponed to a higher level, and that, when it does occur, it is carried out by a vast number of cells, and in great detail.

What high-level structure awaits our discovery in the brain of man?

2.2 The Perceptron

In our first chapter, we glanced briefly at neurophysiology and abstracted our first model of the brain, the modular net or net of McCulloch-Pitts neurons. The Perceptron group at Cornell University has been working on a slightly different model of the neural net. The main difference is that they have *not* made our assumption that the function of a neuron is fixed for all time. Instead, they allow the weights on each neuron to change with time. The purpose of this is to allow their neural net to change itself with time in such a way as to "learn."

One may think of a perceptron as a pattern-recognition device which is not built to recognize a specified set of patterns, but rather so that it has some ability to "learn" to recognize the patterns of a set after a finite number of trials.

The pattern is presented to the perceptron on a *retina* of

sensory units (e.g., photocells). Although any sensory input may be coded into a form suitable for input to a bank of such sensory units, it is most natural (as the terminology "retina" suggests) to think of the pattern as a visual input of light and shadow. A photocell which receives a relatively light portion of the pattern is activated; one in a relatively dark portion is not.

After our detailed look at the frog retina in Sec. 2.1, it is, of course, clear that this binary response to retinal illumination bears little resemblance to physiological action. The sensory units are connected to *associator units* (formal neurons) which in turn may be connected to each other or to *response units*.

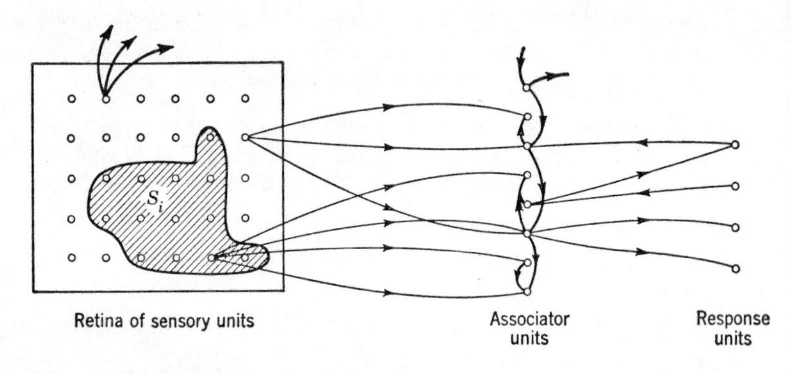

Figure 2.5 Schematic of a perceptron.

In terms of our original neurophysiological consideration of the nervous system as a three-stage system, the retina constitutes the receptors of the perceptron; the associator units comprise the nervous system proper; while the response units are the effectors, or at least correspond to the neurons whose output controls the effectors. It is again consonant with our original considerations that when a *stimulus* is presented to the retina of a perceptron, impulses are conducted from the activated sensory units to the associator units. If the total signal arriving at an associator unit exceeds its threshold, then the associator becomes *active* and sends impulses to the units to which it is connected.

Thus far, then, a perceptron is another embodiment of grossly simplified neurophysiological data on a nervous system with purely visual receptors. However, the Perceptron group has gone further than this, and the additional properties of the net merit discussion here.

REINFORCEMENT RULES: There seems a great deal of evidence that humans have two kinds of memories—"short-term" and "long-term." It further appears that we have to retain an idea for quite a while in short-term memory before it is transferred into long-term memory. The time taken for this transfer has been variously estimated—one estimate is 20 minutes. It appears that if someone goes into coma, his memories of the 20 minutes or so prior to this are lost forever, i.e., they were not transferred to his long-term memory. It is now commonly believed that short-term memory is precisely that type of memory we gave our modular net—the passage of complicated patterns of electrical impulses through the net. It appears, then, that if such transient activity persists long enough it *actually changes the net.* This is best illustrated by a simple example.

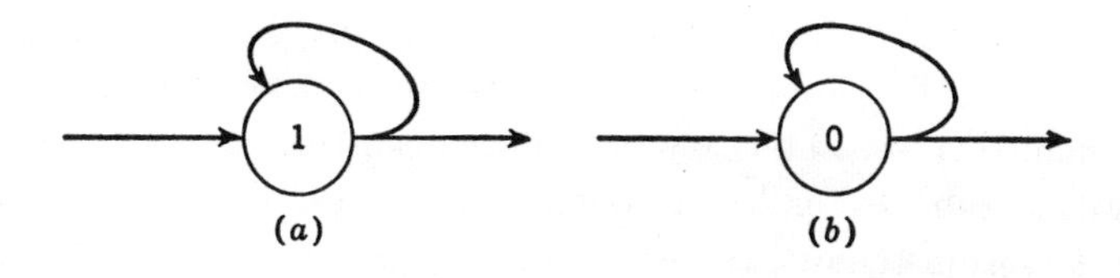

Figure 2.6 A hypothetical example of long-term memory.

The module of Fig. 2.6*a* has a short-term memory of whether its input was ever fired, stored by the impulse reverberating in the loop. It would have long-term memory if the short-term memory could cause its threshold to drop from 1 to 0, for example—for the memory would then be preserved even if the reverberation should die down.

One postulated mechanism for long-term memory is formation of specific proteins within neurons, thus changing their thresholds in response to short-term memory patterns. Another mechanism is that endbulbs grow with repeated use, thus increasing the weight of the corresponding synaptic input and so, it might seem, making it easier to reestablish patterns of impulses using that synapse, hence making the corresponding memory easier to recall! But the precise mechanism is still unknown, and physiology, histology, and anatomy—while encouraging many hypotheses—have yet to deliver a verdict.†

The perceptron is equipped with a long-term memory. This is done by changing the weights of the inputs of neurons or, to put it in the language of the Perceptron group, by changing the magnitude of the impulse carried by a connection. These changes depend on the past activity of the termini of the connection. The rule of this dependence is called a *reinforcement rule*, since it is designed to reinforce the correct responses of the perceptron to stimuli which are presented to it. The physiological evidence being so nebulous, the Perceptron group chose reinforcement rules which were theoretically or experimentally convenient. Their choices have enabled perceptrons to exhibit *aspects* of learning.

RANDOM CONNECTIONS: The Perceptron group has had to decide how they would connect the sensory units to the associator units. A first approach was to make the connections *many-to-many* and *random*. Later they introduced constraints into the network, e.g., subnets for line recognition like those found by Hubel and Wiesel in the cat.

But just as our modular net still had capacity for memory and computation despite the gross simplifications made in its derivation, so early perceptrons exhibited simple learning properties despite the assumptions made in construction. These properties form the material of the remainder of this section.

The Perceptron group has had three main modes of investi-

† For a short discussion of biological memory and an excellent bibliography, see Hans-Lukas Teuber, Perspectives in the Problems of Biological Memory—a Psychologist's View, in F. O. Schmitt (ed.), "Macromolecular Specificity and Biological Memory," The M.I.T. Press, Cambridge, Mass., 1962.

gation: mathematical analysis, simulation on a digital computer, and construction of an actual machine. Each method has its own advantages. One important result of using an actual machine is that it has been found that *neither precision nor reliability of the components is important, and the connections need not be precise.*

Another interesting result is that the perceptron can "learn" *despite trainer error.*

A simple perceptron† is one in which the associator units are not interconnected, *which means that it has no short-term memory!* If such connections do occur, the perceptron is called *cross-coupled.*

Let there be sensory units s_k, associator units a_m, and n stimulus patterns S_i. In this simple model, the connections between s_k and a_m do not change. Therefore, the set of associators activated

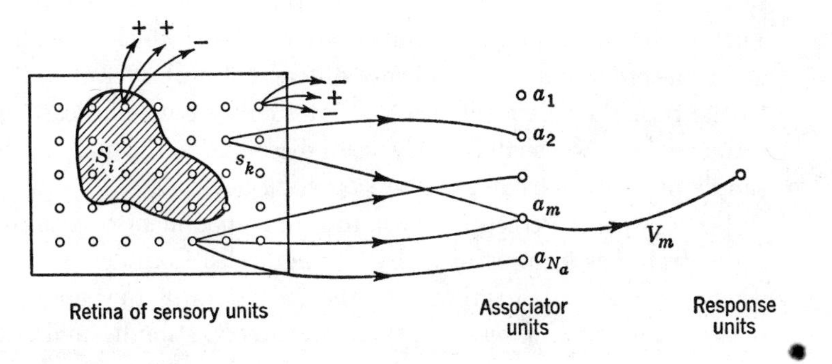

Figure 2.7 Schematic of a simple perceptron.

by stimulus S_i does not change. Let $e_{mi} = 1$ if and only if the associator a_m is activated by stimulus S_i. If we now let V_m be the strength of the input to the response unit from the associator a_m, we have as input to the response unit when stimulus S_i is presented to the retina,

$$u_i = \Sigma_m V_m e_{mi}$$

† H. D. Block, The Perceptron: A Model for Brain Functioning. I, *Rev. Mod. Phys.*, **34**: 123–135 (1962).

Suppose we split our stimuli into 2 classes, +1 and −1. Let r_i be the one of these 2 classes containing stimulus S_i. We want our response element to be activated if and only if the stimulus presented is in class +1.

One assignment of the reinforcement rules is given by the *error-correction procedure*, which is as follows: A stimulus S_i is shown and the perceptron gives a response; if this response is correct, then no reinforcement is made; if the response is incorrect, then the V_m for the *active* associators is incremented by ηr_i (η being a fixed positive number). The inactive associators are left alone. The initial values are arbitrary, say, $V_1^0, \ldots, V_m^0, \ldots, V_N^0$.

Suppose we show the stimuli in an arbitrary sequence, such that each stimulus recurs often. Block† shows that after a certain finite number of steps, the machine will thereafter give the correct responses to all the stimuli so that no further changes take place. Further, he shows that the number of corrections which take place are of the order of n (the number of different stimuli ever presented to the retina). This result shows that the machine can learn by rote, but (as we shall shortly see) discourages the use of the simple perceptron as a pattern-recognition device.

The Mark I Perceptron, a hardware embodiment of a simple perceptron, has a retina of 20 by 20 photocells. Consider the case where we restrict our stimuli to the 26 letters of the alphabet, *each in standard position*—i.e., there are only 26 stimuli—and take our output from five binary-response units ($2^5 = 32 > 26$). In an actual experiment, the machine was reported to learn to identify them correctly after 15 exposures to each letter, a total of 390 exposures. But we require much more of a pattern-recognition system than that it discriminate between stimuli in standard position. What we want is a machine that can recognize each letter wherever it is placed on the retina, even though it be rotated slightly, distorted, and shown against a spotty background. But once we allow this, the number of stimuli jumps alarmingly, as may be seen by considering the motions of a standard letter E, presented as a pattern of dots in the following manner:

† *Ibid.*, pp 129–130.

```
   o o o o o o o
   o o o o o o o
   o o o o o o o
   o o o
   o o o o o o o
11 o o o o o o o
   o o o o o o o
   o o o
   o o o o o o o
   o o o o o o o
   o o o o o o o
   <---- 7 ---->
```

Figure 2.8 A letter E as it might be sensed by the sensory units of a perceptron.

Hence the above result that only of the order of n trials are necessary for rote learning is somewhat vacuous—the simple perceptron is too simple. We have discussed the simple perceptron here for pedagogical reasons—it illuminates a discussion of memory in neural nets. However, it should be realized that more sophisticated work has been done by the Perceptron group. As they set their nets more difficult tasks, so did they build more structure into them. Present work even includes neurochemical research into memory, and formulation of concomitant models.

Before we leave this topic, it is only fair to warn the reader that the perceptron work has received much bitter criticism. Certainly early papers by the Perceptron group made exaggerated claims and must be read with great caution. Further, many workers were alienated by rather unfortunate press-agentry. However, one must be careful not to overreact to the exaggerations by out-of-hand rejection of subsequent work on nets which "learn."

2.3 Structure versus Randomness

The anatomy and physiology of that portion of our brains involved in higher mental activity are little known; although the gross anatomy of the brain reveals a complicated structure, the detailed anatomy yields a bewildering picture of seemingly random interconnections. It appears impossible that our genes specify the exact structure of our brains; rather, it is much more likely that they determine patterns of growth more or less open to the modifying effects of experience. Furthermore, even if the connections were strictly determined, we do not know the mechanism whereby the brain can recognize universals, e.g., recognize the letter A in many positions and despite many distortions (*but see theory in Sec. 4.4*). The reaction of the Perceptron group has been to assume an initial randomness and allow all the structure requisite for pattern recognition to result from changes due to the reinforcement rules. Their approach is interesting and yet, I feel, lacks something. In this chapter, we have looked at the visual system of the frog and found evidence that (in the frog, at least) some very important structure is genetically determined. In Sec. 3.5, we will develop the Cowan-Winograd theory. We will see that if a modular net, designed for a specific function, is transformed to minimize its susceptibility to errors due to the malfunction or death of neurons, the resultant network has a detailed randomness which is closely akin to that found in the detailed anatomy of the brain. As a last argument against the use of complete randomness, we note that there are intellectual acts open to a human child which are forever denied a gorilla—and these must be due, it would seem, to genetically determined differences in structure. Darwinian evolution took aeons to build the capability for pattern recognition into our brains—it would be surprising if a random network should evolve such a capability in a few hours of learning.

However, I must confess that all the above argument supports is this statement: An adequate model of the human brain must be rich in a variety of specific structures, e.g., those involved in the perception of straight lines. It sheds no light on the question: Is structure necessary for learning? In other words, granted that the human brain possesses structure, we have still made no progress in resolving two conflicting points of view, namely—

a. Man is intelligent because evolution has equipped him with a richly *structured* brain. This structure, while serving a variety of functions, in particular enables him to learn. A certain critical degree of structural complexity is required of a network before it can become self-modifying—no matter how sophisticated its reinforcement rules—in a way that we could consider intelligent.

b. Man is intelligent because evolution has equipped him with a richly *interconnected* brain. The pattern of interconnections is irrelevant to truly intelligent learning, which results from the action of reinforcement rules on a sufficiently huge, but essentially random, net.

Perhaps the truth lies in a subtle blend of these views. The search for that blend will be one of the most exciting quests in the future of this subject.

3

The Correction of Errors in Communication and Computation

The individual neurons of the brain are prone to many malfunctions. Further, several thousand neurons in a human brain die every day and are never replaced. It is thus of great interest to understand how the brain can function with any stability and precision. The main aim of this chapter is to introduce the reader to the Cowan-Winograd theory of functionally stable automata—modular networks which function reliably despite modular malfunction. This theory relies heavily on Shannon's well-known theory of communication in the presence of noise. We thus devote a large part of this chapter to a treatment of Shannon's theory—a theory of great independent interest and importance.

3.1 Reliable Brains from Unreliable Neurons

This section is devoted to a brief survey of some neurological data which point up the fact that the brain functions with precision and stability, despite neuronal death or malfunction. We quote extensively from a review paper by W. S. McCulloch, M. A. Arbib, and J. D. Cowan:†

For reasons of economy we have adhered strictly to an electrical hypothesis of central inhibition and excitation. This requires that the electrical properties of transmission and the geometry of the structures determine the output as a specific function of the input to each tissue.

Perhaps the simplest example of this unique correspondence of structure to function is located in the superior olive [Fig. 3.1] whose

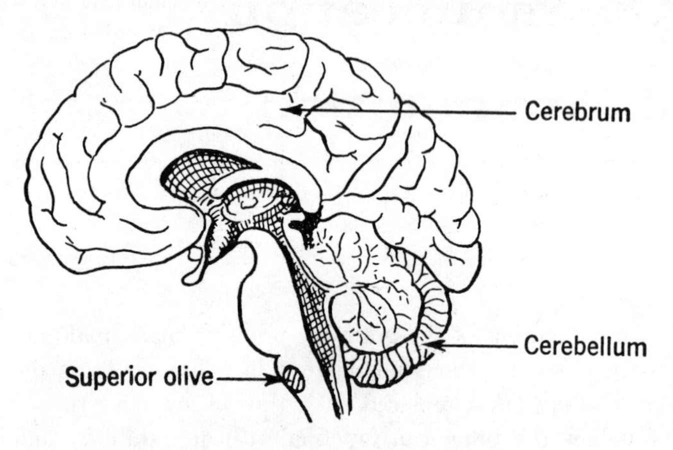

Figure 3.1 The human brain in cross section.

large cells receive signals from both ears. The anatomy of these cells, and of the synapses upon them, is such that signals from either ear alone excite them; whereas contemporaneous signals from the two ears cancel each other, leaving the cell unaffected. By these cells we detect the directionality of a sound, and hear a signal in one ear despite a large common background noise in both.

A second clear example is to be found in the cerebellum [Fig. 3.1] which evolved from an arch of large cells, each receiving signals from the

† Neurological Models and Integrative Processes, in M. C. Yovits, G. T. Jacobi, and G. D. Goldstein (eds.), "Self-organizing Systems, 1962," Spartan Books, Washington, D.C., 1962, pp. 49–59.

vestibular organs of both ears, and conveying information on the accelerations of the head. The input has come to include signals from almost all parts of the body and from the rest of the brain. They arrive on a host of small cells whose fine and uniform axons divide to run transversely through the branches of the giant cells, as wires through parallel rows of regularly spaced telephone poles, many thousands of wires contacting each pole in its row. The cerebellum serves as an interval clock in all our ballistic acts, such as fiddling or writing, in which accelerations and decelerations must be precisely equated and timed—at intervals too brief for reflexes to mediate the process.

Our reason for considering the superior olive and the cerebellum is that the function of the tissue does not inhere in any particular neuron but is distributed over all the neurons. Anatomically, this is recorded in the multiplication of similar components and in the multiplication of overlapping inputs. Physiologically, it is obvious in the time domain, for both tissues operate, one in detecting and the other in timing, with a precision of 1–2 μsec.; whereas the components, either in detecting coincidences or in emitting impulses, have a standard deviation greater than $\frac{1}{3}$ msec. Pathologically it follows from the negligible loss of precision, despite the scattered death of one-tenth of the cells. *We emphasise that both superior olive and cerebellum exhibit a stability of performance greater than that of their components even though each component is computing essentially the same function, albeit of a somewhat different set of inputs.*

Before continuing with our quotations, we must introduce some new ideas. The inputs to a neuron are called afferents. By *interaction of afferents*, we mean the situation, shown schematically in Fig. 3.2, whereby an afferent does not excite or inhibit

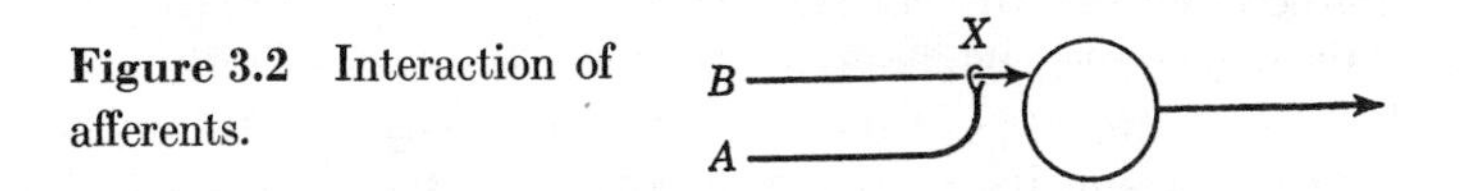

Figure 3.2 Interaction of afferents.

the neuron, but acts to block an impulse in another afferent. Thus, if in the figure an impulse traveling along B reaches X at the same time as an impulse along A, its passage is blocked; whereas if no impulse meets it, it continues its passage and proceeds to excite or inhibit the firing of the neuron.

By a Boolean function,† we mean a function $f(x_1, \ldots, x_n)$ whose arguments and values may only range over the two numbers 0 and 1. Thus we may consider the input-output relation of a McCulloch-Pitts neuron to be a Boolean function. It is easily shown that there are many Boolean functions which cannot be computed by a McCulloch-Pitts neuron [e.g., $f(0,0) = f(1,1) = 1$; $f(0,1) = f(1,0) = 0$]; whereas if we allow our formal neurons to have interaction of afferents, we may, given *any* Boolean function, construct a formal neuron which computes it.

There is reason to believe that the precise location and sequence of connections to dendrites and cell bodies, as well as the interaction of afferents determined by their juxtapositions, specify what function each cell is to compute at a particular threshold when the signals it receives are at specific strengths and specifically timed. As every experimental neurophysiologist knows to his sorrow, there is no reason to believe that any one of these is exactly determined by our genes, by adaptation, or by learning.

Let us begin with the detailed synapsis of our 10^{10} neurons which can scarcely be specified by our genes under fixed proper environmental conditions. Neuroanatomists generally believe that an appreciable number of axons normally grow astray. Estimates of 1 per cent, or more, are commonly made for various structures. Adjacent similar columns of cells in the cerebral cortex are never exactly alike in their anatomical pictures, and it seems reasonable to believe that, while their synapsis is generally specified, the details are left largely to chance. Even if synapsis were specified in detail, the random death of at least one neuron a minute would soon disorder the details. Myelination‡ of finer axons, at least in the outer layers of the cerebral cortex, continues to at least the 50th year of life. Moreover, the brain exhibits visible pulsations with respiration, and with heartbeat, and also at a higher frequency, recently attributed to rhythmic contractions of glia.‡ Certainly a living brain has no fixed or rigid geometry.

When we turn to other parameters affecting nervous activity, we note

† Named after George Boole, who first studied their use in mathematical logic in 1840.

‡ Myelination is the formation of an "insulating sheath" around the axon of a neuron. The cells which comprise this sheath are the glial cells.

that many general chemical changes alter all components similarly. For example, homeostatic mechanisms† tend to keep the brain at a pH of approximately 7.2. If it rises to 7.4, the threshold of neurons, soma and axon, falls to approximately 50 per cent of the normal value, at which high pH, one begins to have spasm of the palms of the feet and hands. When the pH falls to 7.0 the thresholds rise 100 per cent. These are little more than the changes one can induce safely by hyperventilation and by holding one's breath, and neither of them prevents a diver from performing complicated tasks. Under surgical anaesthesia with ether, the pH of the brain is approximately 6.9, but the respiration continues automatically.

Finally, thresholds and strengths of impulses are sensitive to temperature. Yet human brains have been known to work, albeit not too well, at 42°C, not far beneath the lethal temperature. Below 26°C (*body* temperature, not room temperature), mammalian nervous tissue becomes unexcitable—but at several degrees above this temperature, patients, chilled for cardiac surgery, can still think.

It has long been known that bursts of high frequency in nerve cells and their axons affect their recovery time and, consequently, both their thresholds and the strength of their impulses. Moreover, during recovery, their voltage gradients are known to affect other neurons in the vicinity. These effects are large and are easily demonstrated when many components are fired in unison. They must occur normally, to some extent, and may well account for much of the large fluctuation of threshold which we detect in them; but whether these jitters, say some 10 per cent of threshold, are used in signalling or are only noise has not yet been determined.

Be that as it may, one has to admit the possibility of many local random changes for reasons like those given above, and for many little accidents. Finally, since every trigger point is a small area of high specific resistance and must operate at body temperature, the threshold must jitter.

In any case, an adequate neurological model must be designed to function properly despite local random variations.

In constructing an adequate neurological model, we have also to cope with two further causes of error. The first occurs in the case of dying neurons; often in disease, these neurons emit

† Compare Sec. 4.3.

long trains of impulses when there should be none and, when dead, emit none when there should be some. The second occurs as scattered distribution in time and place of impulses arising spontaneously in axons or their failure to propagate for no good reason.

3.2 Von Neumann's Multiplexing Scheme

The discussion of the last section makes it abundantly clear that we need to understand how a modular network can function reliably despite malfunctions of the individual neurons. This need is heightened by the following simple calculation: Consider a chain of n modules and assume that there is a probability p of malfunction for each neuron. Then the probability that the output of the chain is correct is, to a first estimate, $(1 - p)^n$. Now no matter how small p is, $(1 - p)^n$ gets to a ½ when n is made large enough†—and if our output is equally likely to be right or wrong, it is of no use to us! We again conclude that if we are considering modular nets in which—as a better approximation of reality in our brain model—we allow modular malfunction, some form of error correction is necessary.

Perhaps the first to construct a model of this type was John von Neumann in his paper "Probabilistic Logics and the Synthesis of Reliable Organisms from Unreliable Components."‡

Von Neumann considered two schemes for constructing a reliable automaton from less reliable components. In each case, he allowed only one type of component—we shall here discuss the scheme in which the basic component is the Sheffer stroke module $(a \mid b)$.§ It has two inputs, a and b, and

† If p is 0.01 (1 per cent), then n has to be about 70—not an unreasonable depth for a brain with 10^{10} elements!

‡ C. E. Shannon and J. McCarthy (eds.), "Automata Studies," Princeton University Press, Princeton, N.J., 1956, pp. 43–98.

§ The Sheffer stroke module is *universal* in that any finite automaton behavior can be realized, in the sense of Theorem 1.3.1, by a net of such modules.

$$(a \mid b)(t+1) = 0 \quad \text{if and only if } a(t) = 1 \text{ and } b(t) = 1$$

That is, $(a \mid b)$ is equivalent to not a or not b.

With each of these modules he associated a probability of malfunction p, which was independent of the inputs. To minimize the effect of these malfunctions, he used the following technique, known as "multiplexing":

a. Replace each line of an automaton by a bundle of n lines.
b. Replace each module by n modules.
c. Operate on each bundle with a "restoring" organ.

The signals carried by each bundle are coded as follows: Each line carries a 1 or a 0. Let the excitation level (i.e., number of ones) in any bundle be k. Choose $\Delta < \frac{1}{2}$, and then let $k \geq (1 - \Delta)n$ signal a 1, $k \leq \Delta n$ signal a 0, and any intermediate value signal a malfunction. We call such a Δ the *fiduciary level*, i.e, the level fixed as our basis of comparison.

The restoring organ operates in the following manner: Any bundle signal whose excitation level k is greater than a certain critical value k_c has this level increased by the restoring organ; conversely, any signal whose excitation level is lower than k_c has this level decreased by the restoring organ. The function of the restoring organ is sketched in Fig. 3.3.

To minimize the chance of a systematic buildup of errors, all bundles are randomized between switching operations. For

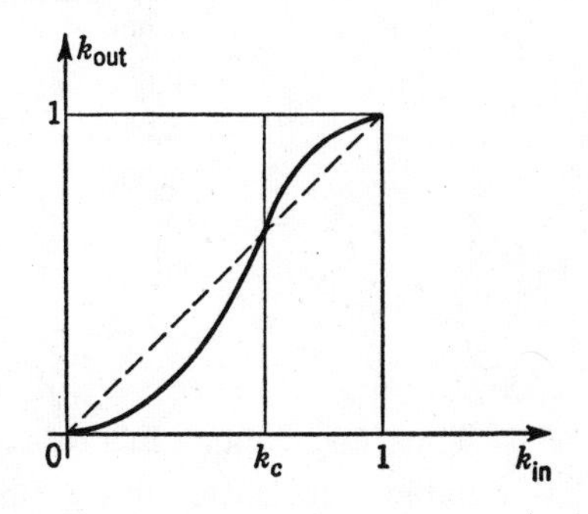

Figure 3.3 The function of the restoring organ. k_{in} = fraction of inputs firing; k_{out} = fraction of outputs firing.

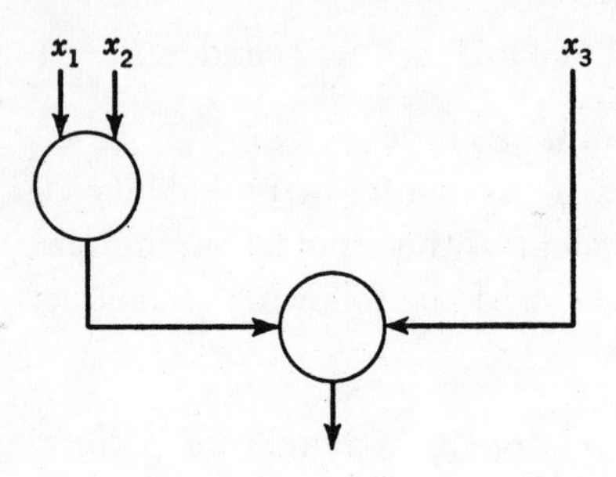

Figure 3.4 A "precursive" network.

example, the automaton shown in Fig. 3.4 is replaced by the automaton shown in Fig. 3.5.

The restoring organ is itself composed of $2n$ noisy Sheffer stroke modules.

Under the assumption that no error is introduced by splitting lines, von Neumann showed that for $p < 0.0107$, the probability of malfunction of the automaton

$$p_n \sim an^{-1/2}10^{-bn} \tag{3.2.1}$$

where a and b are constants and so may be made arbitrarily small by increasing n. The constants are such, however, that rather large values of n were required to obtain reasonable small p_n's, e.g., with probability of malfunction of single component $p = 1/200$,

n	p_n
1,000	2.7×10^{-2}
2,000	2.6×10^{-3}
3,000	2.5×10^{-4}
5,000	4.0×10^{-6}
10,000	1.6×10^{-10}
20,000	2.8×10^{-19}
25,000	1.2×10^{-23}

Thus von Neumann's solution has this defect: To construct a reliable automaton using his solution requires a very high

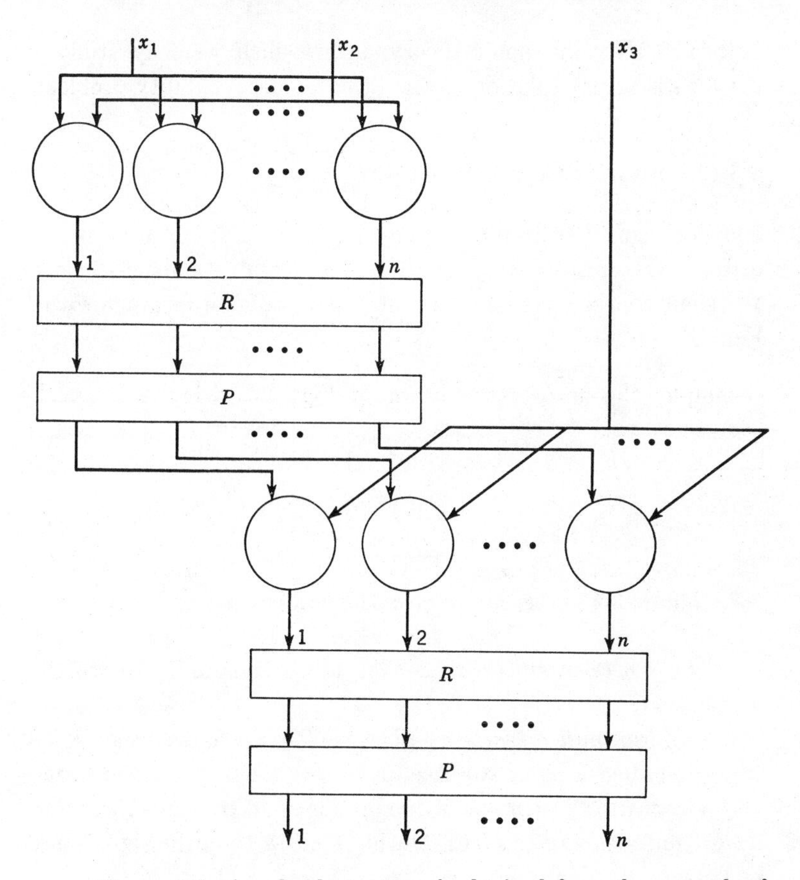

Figure 3.5 A redundant network obtained from the network of Fig. 3.4 by the von Neumann multiplexing scheme. R = restoring organ; P = random permutation.

order of redundancy. Furthermore, the resultant automaton possesses a particular structure which does not appear to correspond to any known biological structure—a sad fault in a brain model.

Von Neumann himself was not very happy about his mode of solution and was of the opinion that "error should be treated by thermodynamic methods and be the subject of a thermodynamical theory, as information has been by the work of L. Szilard and C. E. Shannon." With this in mind, we devote our attention in Sec. 3.3 to Shannon's theory, after which we may study a more satisfactory solution to the brain-model reliability problem.

3.3 Shannon's Communication Theory†

The problem of transmitting messages in the presence of static, disturbance, or other forms of "noise" is the subject of this theory. We shall consider communication systems of the form shown in Fig. 3.6.

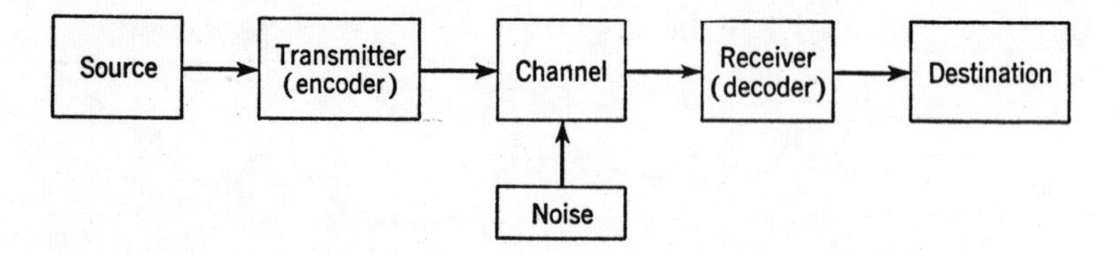

Figure 3.6 Schematic of a communication system.

The *source* produces a message to be communicated to the destination.

The *transmitter* (*encoder*) operates on the message in some way to produce a signal suitable for transmission over the channel.

The *channel* is merely the medium used to transmit the signal from transmitter to receiver. During transmission the signal may be perturbed by interference ("noise").

The *receiver* (*decoder*) is the inverse of the transmitter.

The *destination* is the person or thing for which the message is intended.

Here we study only the "discrete" case, i.e., the case where messages and signals are regarded as sequences of symbols. Our whole aim in this section is to prove Shannon's theorem, which provides very broad conditions under which we may choose our transmitter so that, despite noise, the message sent can be received as accurately as desired.

Weaver, in his excellent and stimulating discussion of com-

† Often referred to as Information Theory.

munication theory, sees the problems of communication falling into 3 classes:

Technical problems: How accurately can the symbols of communication be transmitted?

Semantic problems: How precisely do the transmitted symbols convey the desired meaning?

Effectiveness problems: How effectively does the received meaning affect conduct in the desired way?

Shannon's theory deals with only the technical problem. To this end, messages will be characterized by their probabilities without regard for value or meaning. It might be objected that a treatment which takes no consideration of the last two problems is unrealistic and even misleading. Yet I should prefer to say that the study of the technical problem is a first step, but by no means the last one. We cannot convey our meaning or purpose with any accuracy over a system which transmits symbols inaccurately. For this reason, it is worthwhile to master the technical problem first.

A rather general treatment of Shannon's theory entails the use of such concepts as measure theory, ergodic theory, and martingales. Such a treatment is given by A. I. Khinchin in "Mathematical Foundations of Information Theory,"† but is too sophisticated and much too lengthy for inclusion here. Instead, we follow Shannon's approach by characterizing our source as a Markov process, by letting our channel be memory-less, and by omitting details of rigor in our mathematical proofs.‡

† Dover Publications, Inc., New York, 1957. Another, more recent, technical treatment is given in A. Feinstein, "Foundations of Information Theory," McGraw-Hill Book Company, Inc., New York, 1958.

‡ This section has been largely taken from C. E. Shannon, The Mathematical Theory of Communication, *Bell System Tech. J.*, **27**: 379–423; 623–656 (1948). This basic reference has been made available in book form in C. E. Shannon and W. Weaver, "Mathematical Theory of Communication," The University of Illinois Press, Urbana, Ill., 1949, which also contains Weaver's essay "Recent Contributions to the Mathematical Theory of Communication."

In Sec. 3.3.1, we shall make a definition for a mathematical measure of information which depends only on the probabilities of the messages involved.

In Sec. 3.3.2, we shall set up our mathematical model of the source and channel. We shall associate with our source an *entropy* H, which is to be thought of as the average amount of information contained in each symbol emitted by the source. Shannon uses the word "entropy" to designate this amount since the formula for it is analogous to that for the entropy of statistical mechanics. How far this formal analogy may be pushed is still open to controversy. The reader is warned against careless use of the analogy.

The channel will transmit the symbols emitted by the source one by one, the noise perturbing the symbols independently. Because the present output depends on the present input and not on past inputs, we call the channel memory-less. The perturbation will clearly result in a loss of information in the channel. In Sec. 3.3.3, we shall study the average amount of information getting through the channel per symbol—called the *transmission rate* R. Clearly $R \leq H$, since we cannot receive more information than is sent. H-R is called the *equivocation*, since we may regard it as the amount of uncertainty we have about the original message. R is different for different sources. We define the *capacity* C *of the channel* as the maximum value of R we can obtain by suitable choice of source. C is thus the maximum amount of information per symbol that we can ever hope to transmit through our channel.

It may seem surprising that we should define a definite capacity C for a noisy channel, since we can never send certain information in such a case. It is clear, however, that by sending the information in a redundant form the probability of errors can be reduced. For example, by repeating the message many times and by a statistical study of the different received versions of the message, the probability of errors could be made very small. One would expect, however, that to make this probability of errors approach zero, the redundancy of the encoding must increase indefinitely, and the rate of transmission therefore approach zero. This is by no means true. If it were, there would not be a very well-defined capacity for a given frequency of errors or a given equivocation, the capacity going down as the error requirements are made more stringent. Actually the capacity C defined above has a very definite significance. It is possible to send information at the rate C through the channel *with as small a frequency of errors or equivocation as desired* by proper encoding. This statement is not true for any rate greater than C. These results are the main justification for the definition of C, and constitute Shannon's *remarkable* Fundamental Theorem for a Discrete Noisy Channel:

Let a discrete channel have the capacity C and a discrete source the entropy H. If $H \leq C$, there exists a coding system such that the output of the source can be transmitted over the channel with an arbitrarily small frequency of errors (or an arbitrarily small equivocation). If $H > C$, it is possible to encode the source so that the equivocation is less than $H - C + \epsilon$ where ϵ is arbitrarily small. There is no method of encoding which gives an equivocation less than $H - C$.

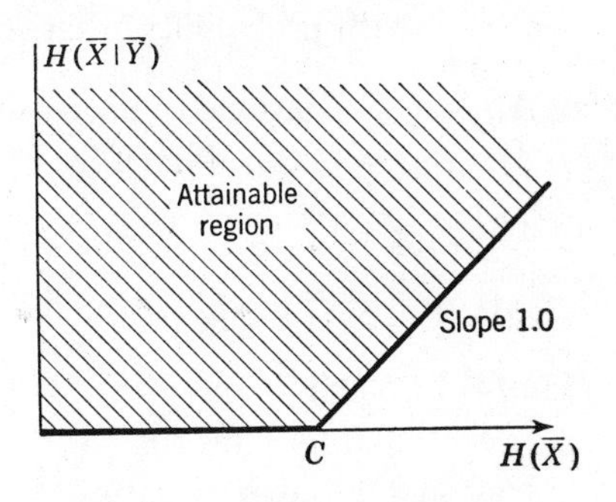

Figure 3.7 Graphical presentation of Shannon's Fundamental Theorem for a Discrete Noisy Channel. Any point above the heavy line in the shaded region can be attained, and those below cannot. The points on the line cannot in general be attained.

The proof of this fundamental theorem is given in Sec. 3.3.4. I cannot overemphasize the fact that this theorem is truly remarkable. Should it not appear so at first sight, it deserves a careful re-reading in the context of our present discussion.

The detailed definitions and the proof of Shannon's theorem do require a certain facility with the theory of probability, and so may be inaccessible to a few readers. Those "nonprobabilists" who do not wish to delve into the details may skip straight to

Sec. 3.3.5. The reader who wishes to understand *why* Shannon's theorem is true should read straight on.

3.3.1 A Measure of Information

Let x be a message with probability p. We wish to find a numerical measure $I(x)$ of *the amount of uncertainty dispelled* (= *the amount of information gained*) when the message x is received. In view of our decision to consider only the technical problem, we assume that $I(x)$ is a continuous function $A(p)$ of p alone. The less likely is x, the greater is the uncertainty dispelled by its occurrence—whence we desire $A(p)$ to be larger if p is smaller. If x_1 and x_2 are independent messages, with probabilities p_1 and p_2, respectively, we desire that the information yielded by x_1 and x_2 (the simultaneous reception of x_1 and x_2—an event with probability $p_1 \cdot p_2$) be the sum of the amounts of information yielded by x_1 and x_2 separately. This motivates the following:

We postulate that the self-information $I(x) = A(p)$ of a message x with probability p satisfies:

a. $A(p)$ is a continuous decreasing function of p, $0 < p \leq 1$.
b. $A(p_1 \cdot p_2) = A(p_1) + A(p_2)$.

Theorem 3.3.1 If $A(p)$ satisfies **a** and **b**, then

$$A(p) = -K \log_2 p \qquad \text{where } K \text{ is a positive constant}$$

Proof Two inductions (one for the numerator and one for the denominator) show that $A(t^r) = rA(t)$ whenever r is a positive rational number. Continuity yields the same result whenever r is a positive real number. Put $t = \frac{1}{2}$ to get

$$A(2^{-r}) = rA(2^{-1})$$

or, in other words,

$$A(p) = A(\tfrac{1}{2})(-\log_2 p) \qquad \text{Q.E.D.}$$

We adopt the usual convention $K = 1$ (choice of unit)†—so

† The unit so obtained is called the "bit"—a contraction of "binary digit"—since a 0 or 1 occurring with equal probability, namely $\frac{1}{2}$, carries one bit of information.

that the result of tossing an unbiased coin yields one unit of information ($-\log_2 \frac{1}{2} = 1$).

Definition 3.3.1 The *self-information* content of a message x with probability p is

$$I(x) = -\log_2 p$$

If $p = 0$, we set $I(x) = 0$.

Suppose we have now a collection of messages

$$\overline{X} = \begin{pmatrix} x_1 & \cdots & x_n \\ p_1 & \cdots & p_n \end{pmatrix}$$

where the ith message x_i has probability p_i ($p_i \geq 0$, $\Sigma p_i = 1$). It now follows from Definition 3.3.1 that the average amount of information obtained on receiving a message from the source

$$H(\overline{X}) \underset{\text{def}}{=} -\sum_i p_i \log_2 p_i$$

where we define $0 \log_2 0$ to be 0. We call $H(\overline{X})$ the *entropy* of the collection.

We have taken pains to render the above definition plausible. However, the real justification for this definition is that the function $-\sum_i p_i \log_2 p_i$ appears in a fundamental role in many basic problems of coding and communication.

3.3.2 Modeling the Source and Channel

We have agreed to characterize messages by their probabilities. Hence we must characterize our source by a probability distribution on the messages it may generate. We use the following characterization of a Markov process:† The source has a finite number of possible "states," $S_1, S_2, \ldots, S_n$. In addition, there is a set of

† This basic concept of probability theory is named for the Russian mathematician A. A. Markov, who first introduced it.

transition probabilities p_{ij}, the probability that if the system is in state S_i it will next go to state S_j. To make this Markov process into an information source, we need only assume that a letter is produced for each transition from one state to another. The states will correspond to the "residue of influence" from preceding letters.†

Among the possible discrete Markov processes, there is a class with special properties of significance in communication theory. This special class consists of the "ergodic" processes, and we shall call the corresponding sources *ergodic sources*. Although a rigorous definition of an ergodic process is somewhat involved, the general idea is simple. In an *ergodic process*, every infinite sequence produced by the process has the same statistical properties. Thus the letter frequencies, pair frequencies, etc., obtained from particular sequences will approach definite limits independent of the particular sequence as the lengths of the sequences increase. Actually this is not true of every sequence, but the set for which it is false has probability zero. Roughly, the ergodic property means statistical homogeneity.

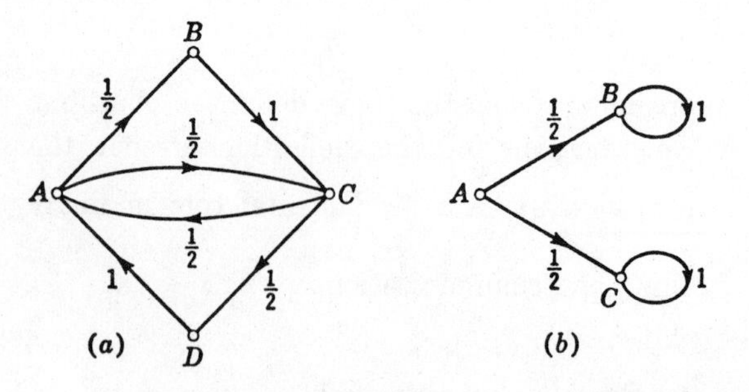

Figure 3.8 Two Markov sources. (*a*) Ergodic; (*b*) nonergodic.

Figure 3.8 shows graphs of two sources, the first ergodic, the second nonergodic (nodes represent states, lines are marked with transition probabilities), where we assume distinct letters associated with distinct transitions.

† The reader may amuse himself by defining "Markov finite automata" (cf. Sec. 1.3).

We may now associate an entropy with our discrete source of the Markov type. For each possible state S_i, there will be a set of probabilities $p_i(j)$ of producing the various possible symbols j. Thus there is an entropy H_i for each state

$$H_i = -\sum_j p_i(j) \log_2 p_i(j)$$

The *entropy of the source* H will be defined as the average of these H_i weighted in accordance with the probability P_i of occurrence of the states in question

$$H = \sum_i P_i H_i = -\sum_{i,j} P_i p_i(j) \log_2 p_i(j)$$

This is *the entropy of the source per symbol of message.*

If we now couple a source S to an encoder, we may consider the combination so obtained as a new source S'. The encoding process simply serves to replace one sequence of symbols by another, encoded, sequence. Thus, the ensemble of messages produced by the new compound source S' has just the same probability distribution as the ensemble of messages produced by the original source S. This implies that the entropy of the source S equals that of S'; i.e., encoding does not change H. It will be well to bear this in mind in Sec. 3.3.4.

If the source is ergodic (we henceforth consider only ergodic sources), the number of times a given path (i,j) in the state graph is traversed in a *long* sequence of length N is about proportional to the probability of being at i, say P_i, and then choosing the path: $P_i p_{ij} N$. If N is large enough, the probability of proportional error $\pm\delta'$ in this is less than ϵ so that for all but a set of small probability, the actual numbers lie within the limits

$$(P_i p_{ij} \pm \delta')N$$

Hence nearly all the sequences have a probability p given by

$$p = \prod_{i,j} p_{ij}{}^{(P_i p_{ij} \pm \delta')N}$$

and $\log_2 p/N$ is limited by

$$\frac{\log_2 p}{N} = \sum_{i,j} (P_i p_{ij} \pm \delta') \log_2 p_{ij}$$

or

$$\left| \frac{\log_2 p}{N} - \sum_{i,j} P_i p_{ij} \log_2 p_{ij} \right| < \delta$$

where δ is small when δ' is. This proves the following:

Theorem 3.3.2 Given any $\epsilon > 0$ and $\delta > 0$, we can find an N_0 such that the sequences of length $N \geq N_0$ fall into two classes:

a. A set whose total probability is less than ϵ

b. The remainder, all of whose members have probabilities satisfying the inequality

$$\left| \frac{\log_2 p^{-1}}{N} - H \right| < \delta$$

In other words, we are almost certain to have $\log_2 p^{-1}/N$ very close to H when N is large.

We now turn to the characterization of the channel. We shall here consider only the simplest model, namely that of the *memory-less discrete channel*, in which successive symbols are independently perturbed by noise. The channel is thus described by the set of transition probabilities $p_i(j)$ [not the $p_i(j)$ of the source], the probability of transmitted symbol i being received as j.

If a noisy channel is fed by a source, there are two statistical processes at work: the source and the noise. There are a number of entropies that can be calculated. First, there is the entropy (per symbol) $H(\overline{X})$ of the input to the channel. There is also an entropy of the output of the channel, denoted by $H(\overline{Y})$. Thus, if s_i is the probability of receiving the ith symbol at the output, then

$H(\overline{Y})$ = the average amount of information gained from each symbol of the output

$$= -\sum_i s_i \log_2 s_i$$

Finally, there are two conditional entropies $H(\overline{Y} \mid \overline{X})$ and $H(\overline{X} \mid \overline{Y})$, which are the entropy of the output when the input is shown and conversely.

Thus if r_i is the probability of the ith symbol being the input to the channel, S_i that of its being the output; if $p_i(j)$ is the probability of the jth symbol being the output of the channel if the ith symbol was the input, while $q_i(j)$ is that of the jth symbol being the input if the ith was the output, then:

$H(\overline{X} \mid \overline{Y})$ = the entropy per symbol of the input ensemble $\overline{X}$ conditioned on the output ensemble $\overline{Y}$

= the average amount of uncertainty we have per symbol of input when we know the output

$$= \sum_i s_i[-\sum_j q_i(j) \log_2 q_i(j)]$$

$$= -\sum_{i,j} s_i q_i(j) \log_2 q_i(j)$$

and, similarly,

$$H(\overline{X} \mid \overline{Y}) = -\sum_{i,j} r_i p_i(j) \log_2 p_i(j)$$

3.3.3 Equivocation and Channel Capacity

If the channel is noisy, it is not in general possible to reconstruct the original message with *certainty* by any operation on the received signal. Rather, what we now consider is ways of transmitting the message in such a way as to *minimize* the effect of noise.

Suppose there are two possible symbols 0 and 1, and we are transmitting at a rate of 1,000 symbols per second with probabilities $p_0 = p_1 = \frac{1}{2}$. Thus our source is producing information at the rate of 1,000 bits per second. During transmission the noise introduces errors so that, on the average, one symbol in 100 is received incorrectly (a 1 as 0, a 0 as 1). What is the rate of transmission of information? Certainly less than 1,000 bits per second, since about 1 per cent of the received symbols are incorrect.

Our first impulse might be to say that the rate is 990 bits per second, merely subtracting the expected number of errors. This is not satisfactory since it fails to take into account the recipient's lack of knowledge of where the errors occur. We may carry it to an extreme case and suppose the noise so great that the received symbols are entirely independent of the transmitted symbols. Then about half of the received symbols are correct, due to chance alone, and we would be giving the system credit for transmitting 500 bits per second while actually no information is transmitted at all. Equally good "transmission" would be obtained by dispensing with the channel entirely and flipping a coin at the receiving point.

Evidently the proper correction to apply to the amount of information transmitted is the amount of this information which is missing in the received signal or, alternatively, the uncertainty when we have received a signal of what was actually sent. From our previous discussion of entropy as a measure of uncertainty, it seems reasonable to use the conditional entropy $H(\overline{X} \mid \overline{Y})$ of the message, knowing the received signal, as a measure of this missing information. Following this idea, the *rate of actual transmission* R would be obtained by subtracting from the rate of production (i.e., the entropy of the source) the average rate of conditional entropy

$$R = H(\overline{X}) - H(\overline{X} \mid \overline{Y})$$

The conditional entropy $H(\overline{X} \mid \overline{Y})$ will, for convenience, be called the *equivocation*. It measures the average ambiguity of the received signal.

In the example considered above, if a 0 is received, the a

posteriori probability that a 0 was transmitted is .99, and that a 1 was transmitted is .01. These figures are reversed if a 1 is received. Hence

$$H(\overline{X} \mid \overline{Y}) = -[.99 \log_2 .99 + 0.01 \log_2 0.01]$$
$$= .081 \text{ bit per symbol}$$

or 81 bits per second. We may say that the system is transmitting at a rate 1,000 − 81 = 919 bits per second. In the extreme case where a 0 is equally likely to be received as a 0 or 1 and similarly for 1, the a posteriori probabilities are ½, ½, and

$$H(\overline{X} \mid \overline{Y}) = -[\tfrac{1}{2} \log_2 \tfrac{1}{2} + \tfrac{1}{2} \log_2 \tfrac{1}{2}]$$
$$= 1 \text{ bit per symbol}$$

The rate of transmission is then 0, as it should be.

The capacity C of a noisy channel should be the maximum possible rate of transmission.

We therefore define the *channel capacity* by

$$C = \text{Max}\ (H(\overline{X}) - H(\overline{X} \mid \overline{Y}))$$

where the maximum is with respect to all possible information sources used as input to the channel.

To elucidate this further, we note that $H(\overline{X})$ depends only on the source, whereas $H(\overline{X} \mid \overline{Y})$ depends on both the source and the channel. If we fix the channel, and vary the source S, then the number

$$R(S) = H(\overline{X}) - H(\overline{X} \mid \overline{Y})$$

= the average amount of information transmitted per symbol by the channel when it is fed by the source S

varies with S. C is simply the maximum of the values that the rate $R(S)$ can assume and thus depends only on the channel.

Before going to the proof of Shannon's theorem, the reader might do well to re-read the material preceding Sec. 3.3.1, where we discussed the significance of the notion of channel capacity.

3.3.4 Shannon's Fundamental Theorem for a Discrete Noisy Channel

We may now restate and prove Shannon's theorem:

Theorem 3.3.3 Let a discrete channel have the capacity C, and a discrete source, the entropy H. If $H \leq C$, there exists a coding system such that the output of the source can be transmitted over the channel with an arbitrarily small frequency of errors (or an arbitrarily small equivocation). If $H > C$ it is possible to encode the source so that the equivocation is less than $H - C + \epsilon$ where ϵ is arbitrarily small. There is no method of coding which gives an equivocation less than $H - C$.

Proof The method of proving the first part of this theorem is not by exhibiting a coding method having the desired properties, but by showing that *such a code must exist in a certain group of codes.* In fact, we will average the frequency of errors over this group and show that this average can be made less than ϵ. If the average of a set of numbers is less than ϵ, there must exist at least one in the set which is less than ϵ. This will establish the desired result.

The capacity C of a noisy channel has been defined as

$$C = \text{Max}\ (H(\overline{X}) - H(\overline{X} \mid \overline{Y}))$$

where $\overline{X}$ is the input and $\overline{Y}$ the output. The maximization is over all sources which might be used as input to the channel. Hence if we are considering a source S with entropy $H < C$, we can choose another source S_0 for which $H(\overline{X}) - H(\overline{X} \mid \overline{Y}) > H$. Suppose S_0 is used as input to the channel. We consider the possible transmitted and received sequences of length T. By Theorem 3.3.2, we may choose T so large that the following four assertions are true:

a. The transmitted sequences fall into 2 classes, a high-probability group with about $2^{TH(\overline{X})}$ members and the remaining sequences of small total probability.

b. Similarly the received sequences have a high-probability set of about $2^{TH(\bar{Y})}$ members and a low-probability set of remaining sequences.

c. Each high-probability output could be produced by about $2^{TH(\bar{X}|\bar{Y})}$ inputs. The total probability of all other cases is small.

d. Each high-probability input could result in about $2^{TH(\bar{Y}|\bar{X})}$ outputs. The total probability of all other results is small.

All the ϵ's and δ's implied by the words "small" and "about" in these statements approach zero as we allow T to increase.

The situation is summarized in Fig. 3.9, where the input sequences are points on the left and output sequences points on the right. The upper fan of cross lines represents the range of possible causes for a typical output. The lower fan

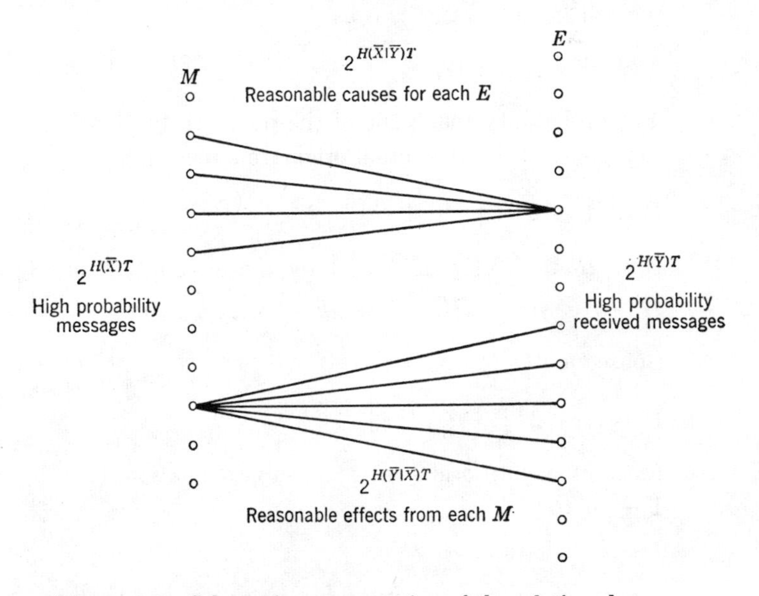

Figure 3.9 Schematic representation of the relations between inputs and outputs in a channel.

represents the range of possible results from a typical input. In both cases, the "small probability" sets are ignored.

Now consider again our source S, producing information at a rate $H < C$. In the period T, this source will have 2TH high-probability messages. We wish to associate these with a selection of the possible channel inputs in such a way as to get a small frequency of errors. We will set up this association in all possible ways (using, however, only the high-probability group of inputs as determined by the source S_0) and average the frequency of errors for this large class of possible coding systems. This is the same as calculating the frequency of errors for a random association of the messages and channel inputs of duration T.

Suppose a particular output y is observed. What is the probability of more than one message from S, in the set of possible causes of y? There are 2TH messages distributed at random in $2^{TH(\bar{X})}$ points. The probability of a particular point being a message is thus

$$2^{T(H-H(\bar{X}))}$$

The probability that none of the points in the fan is a message (apart from the actual originating message) is

$$P = [1 - 2^{T(H-H(\bar{X}))}]^{2^{TH(\bar{X}|\bar{Y})}-1}$$

Now $H < H(\bar{X}) - H(\bar{X} \mid \bar{Y})$ by the assumption on S_0, so

$$H - H(\bar{X}) = -H(\bar{X} \mid \bar{Y}) - k \qquad \text{with } k > 0$$

Consequently,

$$P = [1 - 2^{-TH(X|Y)-Tk}]^{2^{TH(\bar{X}|\bar{Y})}-1}$$

becomes asymptotic [using the approximation $(1 - a)^b \sim 1 - ab$] to

$$1 - 2^{-Tk} \qquad \text{as } T \to \infty$$

Hence, the probability of an error approaches zero and the first part of the theorem is proved.

The second part of the theorem is easily shown by noting that we could merely send C bits per symbol from the source, completely neglecting the remainder of the information generated. At the receiver the neglected part gives an equivocation $H(\overline{X}) - C$ and the part transmitted need only add ϵ.

The last statement of the theorem is a simple consequence of our definition of C. Suppose we can encode a source with $H(\overline{X}) = C + a$ in such a way as to obtain an equivocation

$$H(\overline{X} \mid \overline{Y}) = a - \epsilon \qquad \text{with } \epsilon > 0$$

Then

$$H(\overline{X}) - H(\overline{X} \mid \overline{Y}) = C + \epsilon \qquad \text{with } \epsilon > 0$$

This contradicts the definition of C as the maximum of $H(\overline{X}) - H(\overline{X} \mid \overline{Y})$. Q.E.D.

Actually more has been proved than was stated in the theorem. If the average of a set of positive numbers is within ϵ of zero, a fraction of at most $\sqrt{\epsilon}$ can have values greater than ϵ. Since ϵ is arbitrarily small, we can say that almost all the systems *of the above type* are arbitrarily close to the ideal.

3.3.5 Coding

Shannon's theorem shows that codes exist for transmitting information with a nonzero probability of error as small as desired, but does not tell us how to construct such a code. Much work has been done on constructing actual codes. Let us consider the case where our messages consist of strings of 0's and 1's.

Suppose these digits are generated independently, 0 and 1 appearing with equal probability. Then the rate at which information is produced per symbol is

$$-[\tfrac{1}{2} \log_2 \tfrac{1}{2} + \tfrac{1}{2} \log_2 \tfrac{1}{2}] = 1$$

i.e., 1 bit per symbol. Suppose now we wish to send this sequence over a channel of capacity C, where we shall suppose for the sake of argument that $C < 1$. In that case, we must slow down our rate of transmission so that it is less than C. The encoder and decoder then transform sequences of binary digits into other sequences of binary digits. We replace our 2^k message sequences of length k (i.e., each sequence contains k symbols) by $2^k = 2^{nR}$ signal sequences of length n, where

$$R = \frac{k}{n} < C$$

so that k/n, *the rate of transmission per signal digit*, is indeed less than C.

The encoding operation is performed as follows: The input digits are stored in *blocks* of k digits that are subsequently transformed into an equal number of blocks of signal digits, of length n. By *time redundancy*, we simply mean the above process of taking *more time* to send a suitably coded message. The n blocks are chosen to permit error correction at the decoder. One way of doing this is to send blocks of length n, containing the k digits of the original message, and *n-k check digits*, which later permit the detection and correction of errors incurred during transmission.

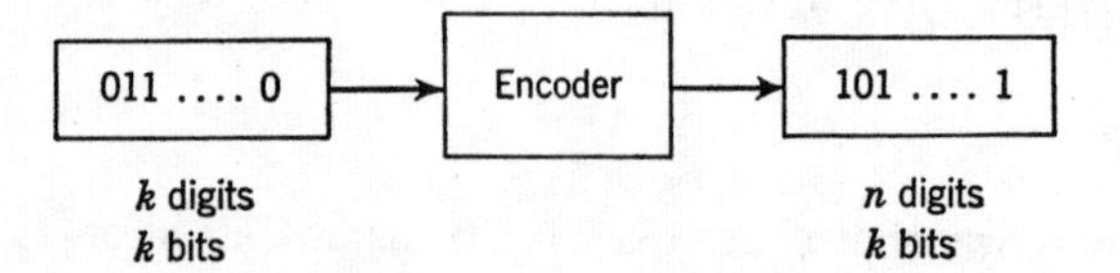

Figure 3.10 Block coding. Note: (1) We have to slow down the input k block so that it enters in the time an n block leaves; (2) there is a delay of time k (on the input scale) in coding since the n block can only be generated after the whole k block enters the encoder.

Any code in which blocks of k digits are encoded into blocks of n digits is called an (n,k) code. The rate of transmission per signal digit in an (n,k) code is k/n.

As examples of error-correcting codes we give three codes invented by R. W. Hamming which correct for single errors at the rates ⅓, ⅖, and 4/7, respectively: Let $a_i (i = 1,2, \ldots, n)$ and $b_j (j = 1, \ldots, n)$ be the transmitted and received signal digits:

$$\underset{\text{message}}{x} \rightarrow \underset{\text{encoded message}}{a} \rightarrow \underset{\text{received message}}{b} \rightarrow \underset{\text{decoded message}}{y}$$

I. Encoding Functions

$$a_1 = x_1$$
$$a_2 = x_1$$
$$a_3 = x_1$$

Decoding Function

$$y_1 = b_1b_2 + b_2b_3 + b_3b_1 \dagger$$

(3,1) code

II. Encoding Functions

$$a_1 = x_1$$
$$a_2 = x_1$$
$$a_3 = x_1 + x_2$$
$$a_4 = x_2$$
$$a_5 = x_2$$

Decoding Functions

$$y_1 = b_1 + (b_1 + b_2)b'$$
$$y_2 = b_5 + (b_5 + b_4)b'$$

where

$$b' = b_1 + b_3 + b_5$$

(5,2) code

III. Encoding Functions

$$a_1 = x_1$$
$$a_2 = x_2$$
$$a_3 = x_1 + x_3 + x_4$$
$$a_4 = x_1 + x_2 + x_4$$
$$a_5 = x_2 + x_3 + x_4$$
$$a_6 = x_3$$
$$a_7 = x_4$$

Decoding Functions

$$y_1 = b_1 + b''$$
$$y_2 = b_2 + b''$$
$$y_3 = b_3 + b''$$
$$y_4 = b_4 + b''$$

where

$$b'' = (b_1 + b_2 + b_4 + b_7)(b_2 + b_5 + b_6 + b_7)(b_1 + b_3 + b_6 + b_7)$$

(7,4) code

The way a Hamming code works is very simple. We illustrate it by considering the (3,1) code. We have $0 \rightarrow 000$, $1 \rightarrow 111$. Let us consider 000, 111 as the points (0,0,0), (1,1,1) in three-dimensional space. They are two vertices of the unit cube (Fig. 3.11).

If at most a single error occurs in transmission, we receive

† The digits here are all binary: 0 or 1. Multiplication is ordinary: $01 = 10 = 00 = 0$, $11 = 1$. Addition is modulo 2 (i.e., we preserve the remainder after dividing the ordinary sum by 2): $1 + 0 = 0 + 1 = 1$, $0 + 0 = 1 + 1 = 0$.

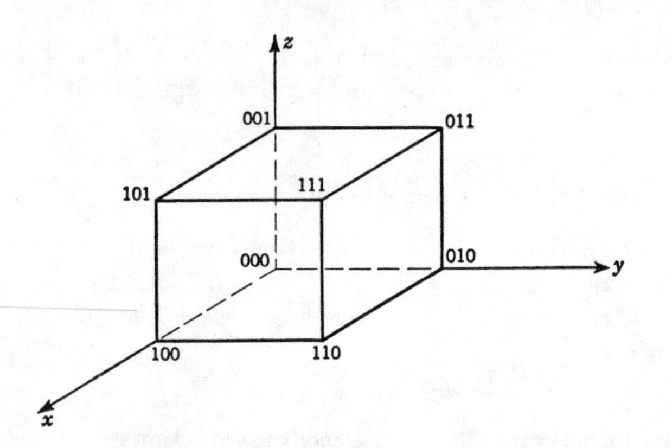

Figure 3.11 The 3-cube.

a message sequence corresponding to the transmitted vertex or one of the vertices immediately adjacent to it. That is,

$$000 \rightarrow 000, 100, 010, \text{ or } 001$$
$$111 \rightarrow 111, 011, 101, \text{ or } 110$$

Now notice that the two "adjacency systems" are disjoint. This is what allows Hamming error correction. The decoding function is merely a logical expression for the "shrinking back" along the edges of the cube to the "transmitted vertex," followed by the operation inverse to the coding.

The (5,2) and (7,4) codes operate similarly, but on the unit cubes in five- and seven-dimensional spaces, respectively.

3.4 Communication Theory and Automata

We translate the redundancy in time, usually associated with a transmission channel, to redundancy of hardware. Instead of having a single channel transmitting the n digits of a block one after the other, we will have n channels transmitting the n bits simultaneously, one bit of the block per channel.

In the channel-redundancy approach, the transmission rate k/n becomes the efficiency ratio, designated by R, which is K/N

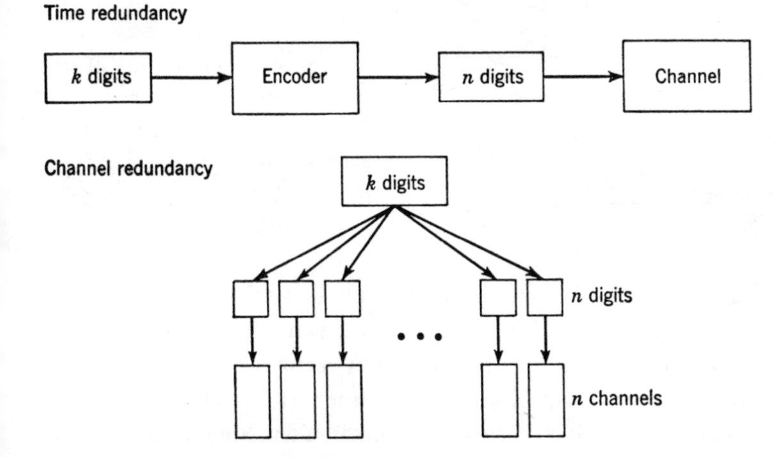

Figure 3.12 Time redundancy versus channel redundancy.

where K is the number of elements we would have used had the elements been noiseless (the number of elements in an irredundant system) and N is the number of elements we do use (the number of elements in the redundant system).

Now let us recall von Neumann's use of *component redundancy* in computing systems (*not* simple communication systems) in order to make them more reliable (cf. Sec. 3.2). We saw that for efficiency ratio $R = \frac{1}{3}n$ [i.e., on replacing a single component by n components, plus a $(2n)$-component restoring organs], the probability of system error was

$$p_n \sim an^{-1/2} \cdot 10^{-bn} \qquad (3.2.1)$$

where a and b are constants.

We may rewrite this as

$$p_n = dR^{1/2}2^{-c/R}$$

where c and d are constants.

This is graphed in Fig. 3.13.

In von Neumann's case, we can only make p_n go to zero by *making R go to zero*, whereas for a communication system, Shannon

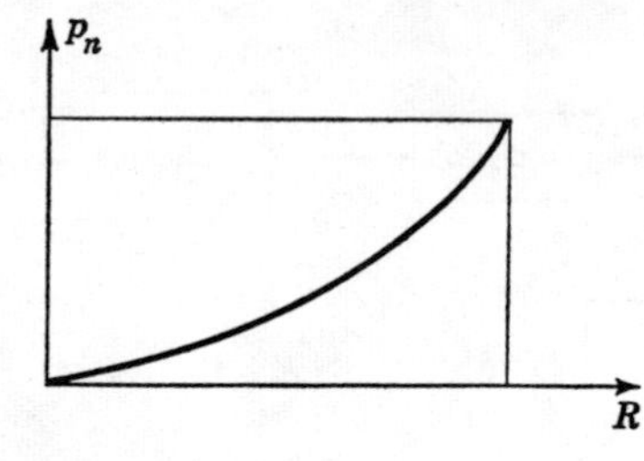

Figure 3.13 Probability of error as a function of efficiency ratio for the von Neumann multiplexing scheme (cf. Fig. 3.7).

showed that codes exist for making p_n arbitrarily close to zero whenever $R < C$. This means that von Neumann's redundant automata do not exhibit noise-free behavior of the type that would permit a capacity *greater than zero* to be defined. The reason underlying this is that the replacement of a module by an aggregate and one connection by a bundle corresponds to the use of an $(n,1)$ code. Only the use of (n,k) codes, in which the ratio $R = k/n$ may be held constant by increasing both k and n, allows positive rates for reliable information processing and hence positive system capacities.

It is therefore natural to consider the possible design of redundant automata that effectively utilize (n,k) codes and exhibit positive computation capacities.

One approach to this problem is evidently to attempt to apply existent techniques of coding theory which essentially consist of "matching" sources to channels in a suitable way and then decoding noisy channel outputs in the manner we have already discussed.

We note that Shannon, in his communication theory, assumed that his encoders and decoders were noiseless—this was

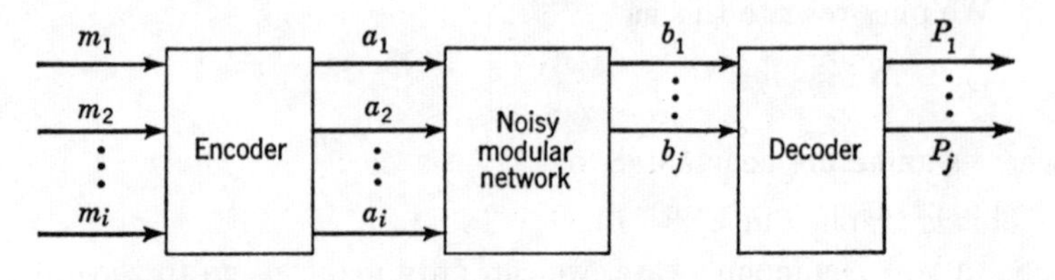

Figure 3.14 A computation system.

justifiable in his case because the amount of noise in, say, radio transmitters and receivers is usually negligible in comparison to the static in the intervening channel. However, in our case, the assumption of noiseless coding and decoding is somewhat dubious—for coding and decoding are computations, and it would be unreasonable to expect the elements of modular coding and decoding networks to be less noisy than those of our computer proper. However, let us for the moment assume that the noise in the encoder and decoder *is* negligible, and hence consider the consequences with P. Elias.†

The modular network (Fig. 3.14) is required to realize the set of events $P_1, \ldots, P_j$ that correspond to logical functions of the inputs $m_1, \ldots, m_i$. The network is composed of modules that compute Boolean functions of one or two variables with small but nonzero probabilities of error. These probabilities are statistically independent of the general state of the network, and of the occurrence of other malfunctions, i.e., we follow von Neumann's error assumption. However, we do not attempt to follow von Neumann in correcting errors by redesign of the network itself. Rather, redundancy is obtained in the signal sequence, as in the communication case. Sequences of length k of the m's are coded into sequences of length n of the a's, which are then fed into the modular net. The output of the net is decoded in blocks of length n to yield blocks of length k which hopefully correspond to the events to be realized. It is important to note, however, that the network is memory-less, and *all processing occurs digit by digit.*

Elias required that each of the inputs $m_1, \ldots, m_i$ be encoded separately and that the decoder be 1:1 in the absence of noise. These assumptions ensure that computation of the prescribed set of events occurs only in the modular network. Otherwise, the analysis would not be very meaningful.

Elias obtained the following results: Of the 16 possible Boolean functions of two inputs m_1 and m_2, only 8 are such that (n,k) codes

† Computation in the Presence of Noise, *IBM J. Res. Develop.*, **2:** 346 (1958).

can be used that realize positive rates of computation with vanishingly small errors. Of these 8, 6 are of little interest, being the functions: (tautology), (contradiction), m_1, $\overline{m}_1$, m_2, and $\overline{m}_2$. The remaining 2, $m_1 + m_2$ and $m_1 \equiv m_2$, are such that Hamming codes can be used. However, these are not "universal" functions (i.e., networks that realize arbitrary Boolean functions cannot in general be constructed from only members of this set) and so the above set of 8 functions is incomplete.

The other set of 8 functions comprising $m_1 \,\&\, m_2$, $m_1 \,\&\, \overline{m}_2$, $\overline{m}_1 \,\&\, m_2$, $\overline{m}_1 \,\&\, \overline{m}_2$, $m_1 \vee m_2$, $m_1 \vee \overline{m}_2$, $\overline{m}_1 \vee m_2$, and $\overline{m}_1 \vee \overline{m}_2$ can only be coded using $(n,1)$ codes. Since this set includes both universal functions (i.e., the Sheffer stroke function $\overline{m}_1 \vee \overline{m}_2$ and the function $\overline{m}_1 \,\&\, \overline{m}_2$), it follows that although networks that realize arbitrary regular events can be constructed from only members of *this* set, they cannot be used to realize such events at positive rates of transmission of information if an arbitrarily small frequency of errors is demanded in the process. This result is essentially similar to that of von Neumann, and Elias *hypothesized* that the computation capacity for reliable processing in arbitrary modular networks was zero, subject to the restrictions imposed upon the ancillary equipment. However, in the next section we shall demonstrate a completely different coding scheme which *does* allow a nonzero capacity.

Let us note that if we relax our condition that no computation occur in the decoder, it is trivial (and quite absurd!) to obtain a nonzero capacity in the following manner: Consider the network to be a very noisy *transmission* channel and so define its capacity in the usual way (check: the definition *does* go through). Then for any rate less than this capacity and any given error probability, choose encoder C' and decoder D' to transmit the original message (= function arguments) through the whole system with great accuracy (and *no* computation). Then pass this output through a noiseless computer D'' which executes the function desired of the original noisy modular net. If we now place encoder C' in front of our noisy net and decoder $D' \rightarrow D''$ after our noisy net, we get error-free computation at any rate

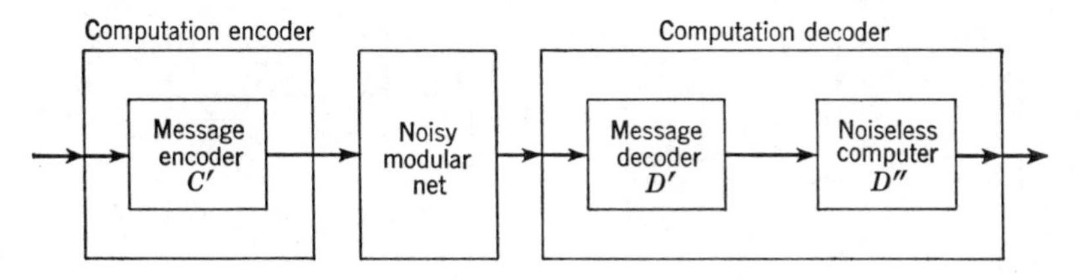

Figure 3.15 Trivial! Absurd! How *not* to design a reliable computation system.

less than capacity. Needless to say, this is *not* a valid solution to our problem.

3.5 The Cowan-Winograd Theory of Reliable Automata

In this section we shall discuss a successful application of the (n,k) codes we studied in Sec. 3.3.5. The work we study is published in the research monograph by S. Winograd and J. D. Cowan "Reliable Computation in the Presence of Noise."†

We saw in Sec. 3.4 that parallel computation (channel redundancy) may take the place of time redundancy and, just as in communication theory we need more and more delay to obtain more and more reliable transmission at a given rate, so in computing do we have to have more and more parallel computation to obtain reliable computation at a given efficiency ratio.

Suppose we are given an automaton A_1 which computes a definite function. To guarantee as much parallel computation as necessary, let us consider (Fig. 3.16*a*) m copies of this automaton—$A_1, A_2, \ldots, A_m$—set side by side, each computing the same function, though not necessarily from the same inputs. Rather than try to construct a reliable automaton to replace A_1 alone, our plan will be to design a new automaton A (Fig. 3.16*b*) to replace the parallel computation of our m automata $A_1, \ldots, A_m$. The efficiency ratio corresponding to this replacement will be

† The M.I.T. Press, Cambridge, Mass., 1963.

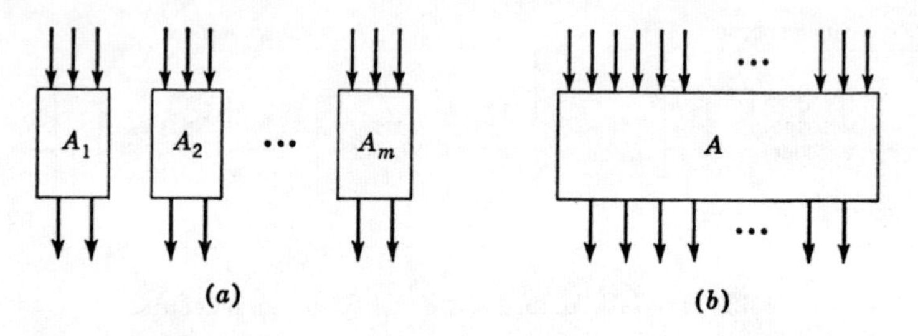

Figure 3.16 (*a*) m irredundant automata computing in parallel; (*b*) 1 irredundant automaton replacing $A_1, A_2, \ldots, A_m$.

$$R = \frac{K}{N} = \frac{m \text{ times the number of elements in } A_1}{\text{number of elements in } A}$$

Before stating the main result of the Cowan-Winograd theory, we must attend to a number of preliminaries.

We must require that A has as output a number of lines, say $O_1, O_2, \ldots, O_m$. But it is clear that any error in the element which emits an O_j will cause an error which cannot be corrected. We call the set of elements which emit the outputs *the last rank*. Hence, Cowan and Winograd say that an automaton can be made to have *arbitrarily high reliability* if its probability of malfunction can be made arbitrarily close to the probability of malfunction in its last rank.

If we regard a module as a *communication* channel, we may define a *capacity* for the module by precisely the methods of Sec. 3.3.3. We shall call the *communication capacity* so computed the *capacity of the module.*

A *definite event* is simply one which can be realized (cf. Sec. 1.7) by a modular network which contains no loops. Thus the result of the computation of a definite event can only depend on a definite number of previous inputs. An *indefinite event* is one which may depend on an indefinite number or earlier inputs, e.g., the event "an input 1 occurred at some time in the past."

We can now state the main result obtained by Winograd and Cowan (Theorem 8.1 of their monograph):

Theorem 3.5.1 Let us be given a definite event. If we have at our disposal all possible formal neurons with interaction of afferents (and thus all possible Boolean functions), each of which has the same capacity C, then for any $R < C$, we can design an "arbitrarily reliable" automaton A which computes the given definite event with efficiency ratio $\geq R$.

Apparently, the requirement that A compute a *definite* event is necessary. M. O. Rabin has shown that no automaton with finite probabilities of going from *any* one internal state to any other can compute a regular nondefinite event. His argument is essentially that if an error ever occurs in one of the feedback loops, it would in general cause all future outputs to be in error. However, since we are only interested in the behavior of automata (e.g., brains) over finite lengths of time (e.g., lifetimes), our automata can be said to compute only definite events, and thus the above theorem's restriction is more mathematical than physical in nature.

The proof of the theorem is by construction and relies on the existence of satisfactory codes for communication channels. Thus there is a definite relationship between the redundancy scheme called for in the proof and communication codes.

We are not going to give a full proof here, but merely run through the main points involved.

The m irredundant automata $A_1, A_2, \ldots, A_m$ placed in parallel constitute our precursive modular network. For the sake of exposition, we make the simplifying assumption that this precursive network (i.e., irredundant noisy network from which we start) is of the highly idealized form shown in Fig. 3.17. This is a modular network of "width" l and "depth" a, whose modules compute the various functions f_{jk} (or realize the events n_{jk}) where $j = 1, \ldots, a$; $k = 1, \ldots, l$. We assume that on the average each module has s inputs and one output which may split into s lines. The inputs of a module in rank $r + 1$ come either from network inputs or outputs of rank r modules.

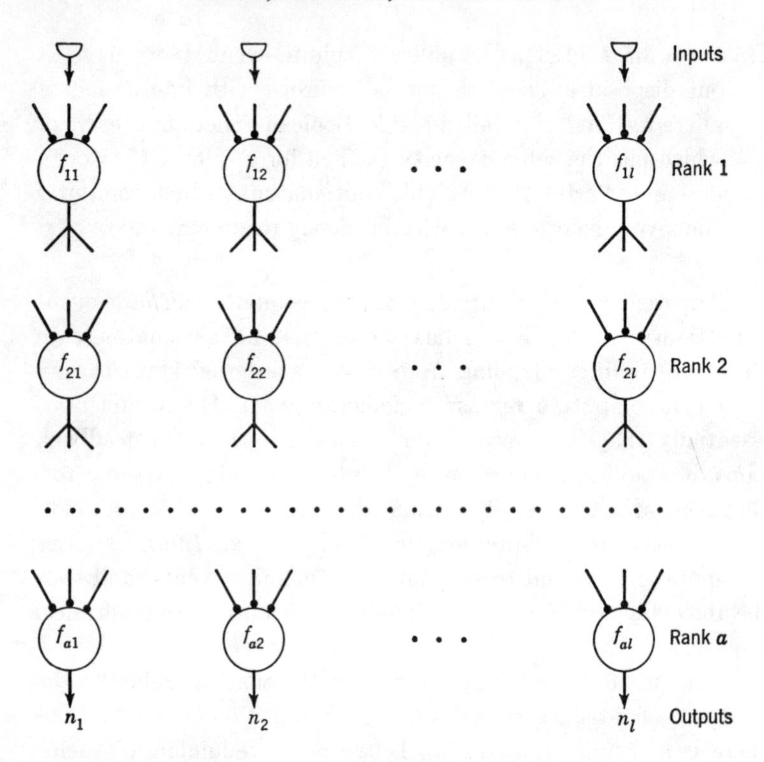

Figure 3.17 A "precursive" modular network.

We want to replace this aggregate of modules by a scheme in which errors are corrected as soon as they occur and in which computation is carried out as soon as the errors are corrected. In other words, we wish to avoid, as far as possible, any propagation of errors. To this end, we shall combine encoding, computing, and decoding in such a way that any given rank of modules decodes its inputs, computes appropriate function, and then encodes its outputs. Note that we are thus carrying out our redundancy coding on the automaton structure and that we are proceeding rank by rank—rank r outputs can only feed into rank $r + 1$ modules.

Before giving the details of the encoding, let us consider the reliability of the precursive modular network of Fig. 3.17. Suppose it is required that the probability—call it P_{a-1}—of at least one malfunction in the first $(a - 1)$ ranks be less than δ. Let ϵ be the probability of malfunction of any module of the network and assume that all malfunctions are independent. Then the probability of *no* malfunction in the first $(a - 1)$ ranks is

$$1 - P_{a-1} = (1 - \epsilon)^{l(a-1)} \tag{3.5.1}$$

Thus, we require

$$\delta \geq P_{a-1} \geq 1 - (1 - \epsilon)^{l(a-1)}$$
$$\sim l(a - 1)\epsilon \qquad [\text{using } (1 - \alpha)^{\beta} \sim 1 - \alpha\beta]$$

That is, approximately

$$\epsilon \leq \frac{\delta}{l(a - 1)}$$

For small fixed δ, this implies that ϵ must decrease as l and a increase. That is, *without suitable coding*, the probability of malfunction in the *precursive* network must decrease as the network increases in size; otherwise the network cannot remain "arbitrarily reliable." In order to obtain arbitrarily reliable networks comprising modules with fixed probabilities of malfunction, we replace the precursive network by another, in which each module computes a new function f'_{mn}. We wish to embody an (n,k) code in this redundant automaton.

Let $n_1(t), n_2(t), \ldots, n_l(t)$ be the definite events realized in general with delay a by the modular network in Fig. 3.17. We shall now describe how these events can be computed with arbitrary reliability by a redundant modular network such as that shown in Fig. 3.18, in which each module computes some Boolean function with delay one. Each of the f'_{mn} incorporates part of an (n,k) code. Assume that the code is of the error-correcting type previously discussed. Let the encoding functions be $e_1, e_2, \ldots, e_n$ and let the decoding functions be $d_1, \ldots, d_k$.

Then the purpose of the elements of the first rank (with functions f'_{1k}) is to carry out some suitable combination of the f_{1j} computations and then encode the results by the e's to yield

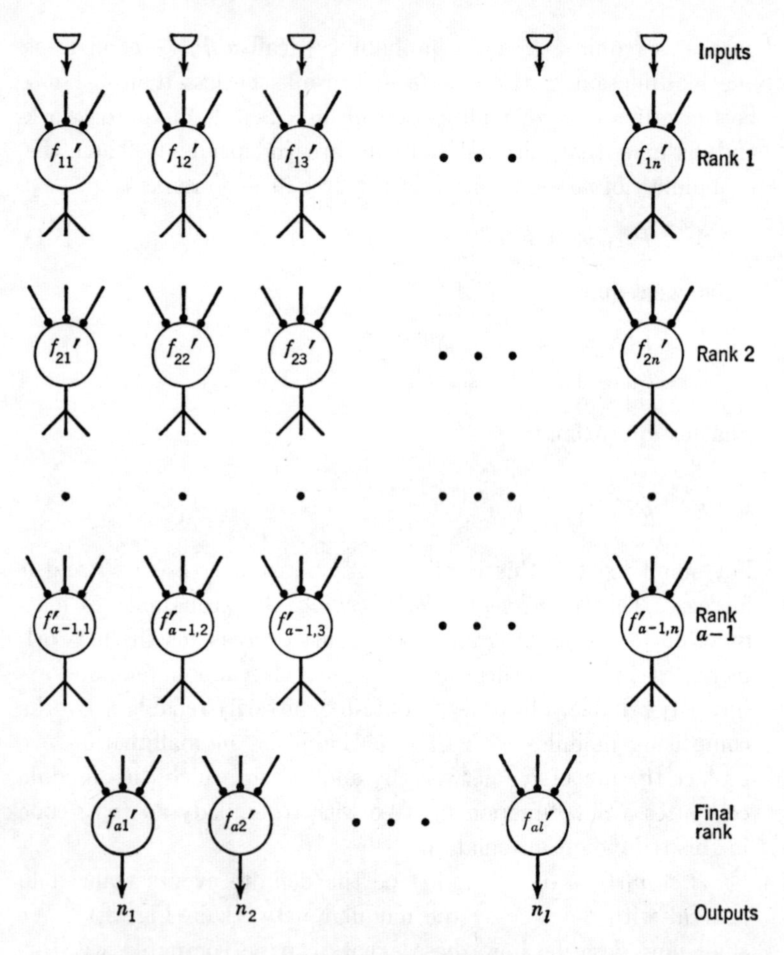

Figure 3.18 A redundant network obtained from the network of Fig. 3.17 by the Cowan-Winograd scheme.

their outputs. The purpose of the elements of any later rank (with functions f'_{ik}, $i > 1$) is to decode the output from the preceding rank using the d's, carry out some suitable combination of the f_{ij} computations, and then use the e's to encode the results for output. There is no encoding in the last rank. In Fig. 3.19, we give a flow graph representation of f'_{mn}.

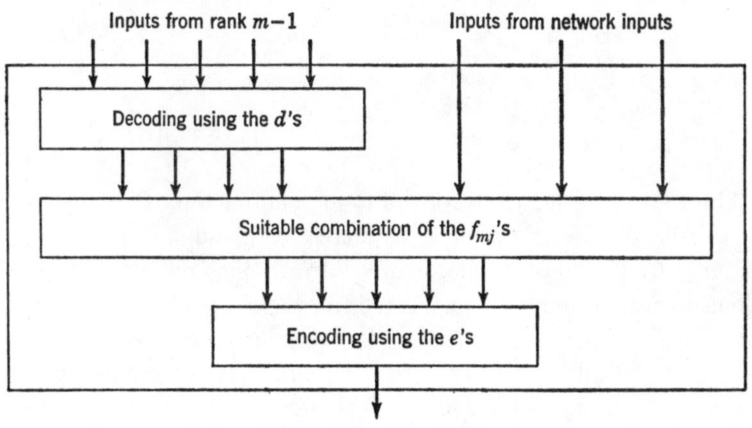

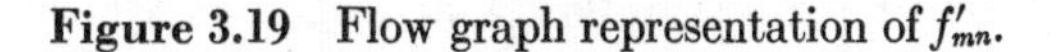
Figure 3.19 Flow graph representation of f'_{mn}.

One may think of the lines between modules as noisy communication channels, before which we want to encode and after which we want to decode. If a line of the bundle comes from a module output, then appropriate decoding must take place, whereas if the line comes from a network input, no decoding is required. Computation is carried out on the result of this evaluation by the f_{mn} (we omit the details of the appropriate connections) to yield a quantity which is then encoded according to the e's. The result is f'_{mn}. In this fashion, we obtain the redundant modular network of Fig. 3.18.

Any rank of this redundant automaton decodes the output of the previous rank and by assumption recovers the "correct" output of the previous rank with some probability of error P_e.

Now Shannon's work is shown by Winograd and Cowan to imply that this error

$$P_e = 2^{k-nC}$$

It follows that the probability of no errors propagating through the first $a - 1$ ranks in the *redundant* network is, recalling the notation preceding (3.5.1), simply

$$1 - P_{a-1} = (1 - 2^{k-nC})^{a-1}$$

That is,

$$P_{a-1} \sim (a - 1)2^{k-nC}$$

Thus, for fixed a, the probability of malfunction P_{a-1} may be made arbitrarily small simply by increasing k and n, while keeping $k/n < C$. Thus, an automaton of arbitrarily high reliability (under our definition) may be constructed from modules of fixed capacity C. The number of modules in the redundant automaton is such that the efficiency ratio is greater than R. This completes our *sketch* of the proof of Theorem 3.5.1.

Note that the number of inputs to the elements required by this redundancy scheme grows larger and larger as we choose more and more complex codes for the basis of the redundancy scheme. This feature of the scheme might block its use with certain types of hardware because one of the requirements is that each element have the same amount of noise. On the other hand, it is evident from our construction that if we impose an upper bound on the number of inputs to the elements, the only way to achieve arbitrarily high reliability for most automata is by letting R go to zero. Thus any scheme for designing arbitrarily reliable automata with finite nonzero R must *apparently* have arbitrarily high complexity of elements.

Because of the increase in complexity of the whole net, it might happen that two elements which are supposed to be connected were not connected in the actual construction of the automaton. The question then arises: How much sloppiness are we to allow the wiring girl? More precisely: With what probability p are we allowed to disregard the blueprint and connect elements that *are not* supposed to be connected and not connect elements that *are* supposed to be connected?

The Cowan-Winograd answer can be summarized in the following theorem (which we make no attempt to prove here—it is Theorem 9.1 of their book):

Theorem 3.5.2 Let A be a blueprint of the *reliable* automaton with efficiency ratio R. Then, if the blueprint is disregarded with a probability *proportional* to (C-R), the resultant automaton will still be arbitrarily reliable.

This theorem can be roughly interpreted as allowing mistakes in the construction of the automaton proportional to the difference between the component capacity and the efficiency ratio. In a sense, we use the added information at our disposal to correct the wiring errors.

As Cowan puts it:

> To recapitulate, we have shown that communication theory may be applied to the problem of designing reliable networks from unreliable components. The resultant functionally redundant automata bear little resemblance to their functionally irredundant precursors. Points to note are:
>
> (a) The multiple diversity of the network . . . each component may perform a mixture of many of the precursive functions and any precursive function is computed by many components. For large enough n, each component may compute an arbitrary mixture of precursive functions;
>
> (b) The heterogeneity of the network . . . this follows immediately from the previous remark;
>
> (c) The efficiency of the network: much smaller component redundancies are needed than in the comparable networks of von Neumann.

Before leaving this fascinating question of ensuring overall reliability in brain functioning, we shall make a few remarks, even though their import can be fully appreciated by the reader only after Chap. 4. Besides coding for reliability within the nervous system proper, we have several built-in devices for increasing our reliability (though not necessarily our trustworthiness!):

a. Our nervous system is connected to effectors. By the very inertia of a moving arm, say, small temporary neuron malfirings are "smoothed out" in our arm motion and so lead to no error in our behavior.

b. Feedback (see Sec. 4.1) with the external world provides a powerful means for compensating for some errors which occur in the brain.

c. Our coding of information within the nervous system is partly in the form of frequency modulation (see Sec. 4.4)—the greater the intensity of a stimulus or desired response, the greater the frequency of the impulse firings in the appropriate nerve fibers. Thus the failure of some neurons at a small percentage of firings may not have the drastic effect one expects in a purely digital (Pitts-McCulloch-type) system, but merely serves to distort slightly the intensities involved.

However important such mechanisms may be in improving the reliability of the nervous system, there still remains the need to construct theoretical brain models—e.g., that of Cowan and Winograd—which embody the desiderata we noted from McCulloch, Arbib, and Cowan in Sec. 3.1. Much, much more is to be learned about the brain and ever more sophisticated brain models await our construction. The Cowan-Winograd theory† provides an important step in our continuing quest.

† For a review of other theories of brain functioning, the interested reader should see the chapter on mathematical theories in D. A. Sholl, "The Organization of the Cerebral Cortex," Methuen & Co., Ltd., London, 1956.

4

Cybernetics

The word "cybernetics" was coined in 1947 by Norbert Wiener and his colleagues to denote "the (comparative) study of control and communication in the animal and the machine." In a sense, then, all that we have discussed so far can be subsumed under the heading of "cybernetics." However, in this chapter we will be primarily interested in questions discussed by Wiener in his book "Cybernetics."†

4.1 Feedback and Oscillation‡

In Sec. 1.1, we considered the nervous system of man as a three-stage system, as shown here again in Fig. 1.1.

† First published in 1948, but I recommend the revised second edition, published by The M.I.T. Press, Cambridge, Mass., and John Wiley & Sons, Inc., New York, 1961.

‡ A good textbook on feedback systems is J. C. Gille, M. J. Pélegrin, and P. Decaulne, "Feedback Control Systems," McGraw-Hill Book Company, Inc., New York, 1959, 793 pages. An excellent set of articles for the "intelligent layman" on feedback and its uses is given in the *Scientific American* book, "Automatic Control," Simon and Schuster, Inc., New York, 1955.

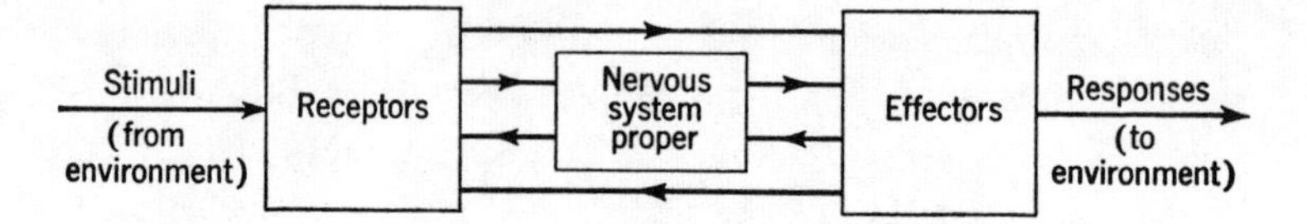

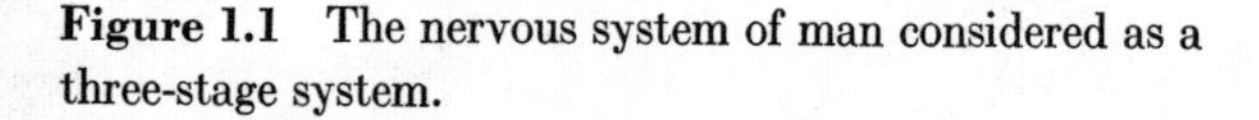
Figure 1.1 The nervous system of man considered as a three-stage system.

So far, we have restricted our attention to problems concerning the structure of the nervous system proper (the modular networks of McCulloch and Pitts, the perceptron, and the Cowan-Winograd theory) and to a brief discussion of the arrow receptors → nervous system (the visual system of the frog). We might say that we have studied and modeled the brain in isolation, but have not seen how it interacts with the effectors. If we give a finite automaton the power to interact with its environment by providing it with a tape scanner-printer-mover, it becomes a Turing machine, and has significant new properties (cf. Sec. 1.7). We may thus expect that, if we extend our view of the nervous system to include effector-receptor interactions, we may obtain significant new insight.

To this end we now turn our attention to the arrow effectors → receptors. We see that information can be *fed back* to the nervous net proper as to how effectively it is controlling the activity of the effectors.

Let us make this clear by two simple examples.

a. If I wish to pick up a pencil, I move my hand toward it. My eyes then tell me how far my hand has to move. My brain thus continually gets information from my receptors (eyes) to tell me the position of my effector (hand). It can then compute appropriate instructions to issue to my arm muscles to move my hand in such a way as to reduce the difference between the actual and desired position of my hand (on the pencil).

b. When I walk, I alternately lift a foot and then let it fall. I control the muscle flexions in my leg to "change step" when the pressure exerted on my foot by the ground exceeds a certain critical value. Thus the position of my effector (foot) relative to the ground is *fed back* to my brain by my receptors (pressure-sensitive nerves in my foot). Once again, it is a difference—between the position of my foot and the ground—that is the crucial determinant of the instructions that my brain issues to my leg muscles. The importance of this "feedback" from the pressure receptors of the feet is well illustrated by the following common experience: After sitting cross-legged for a long time, one gets up only to find that one has "pins and needles" and has to walk without the use of pressure feedback—as a result, the leg movements are clumsy and uncoordinated.

The conclusion we draw from these two examples is that the arrow effectors → receptors plays a crucial role in determining our responses. In other words, the concept of *feedback* must play an essential role in our study of brains and machines, where we say that an organism or a machine has feedback if its activity is controlled to some extent by the comparison of its actual performance with some tested performance. In particular, as our example of the hand and pencil showed, we are particularly interested in *negative* feedback, in which the machine uses the feedback to *decrease* the difference between actual and desired performance.

A simple example of negative feedback in machines is afforded by the thermostat, which serves to decrease the difference between actual performance (the temperature of the room) and desired performance (the temperature setting on the control of the thermostat) by suitably controlling the heat production of a furnace.

We may diagram a simple negative feedback system as shown in Fig. 4.1.

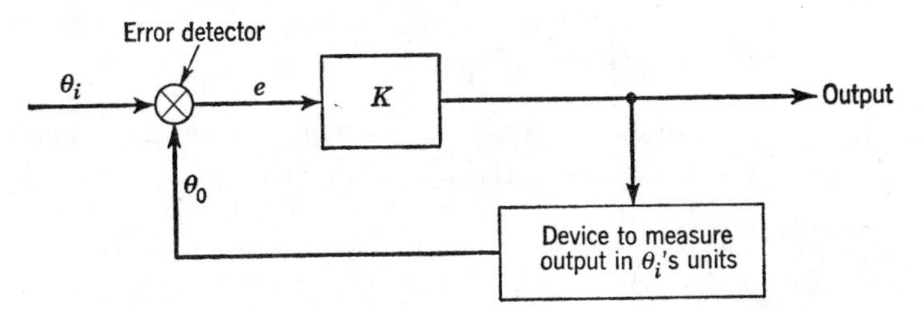

Figure 4.1 A feedback system.

We continually feed into the system a quantity θ_i which indicates the measure of the desired output. Now consider the actual output. We feed back its measure θ_0 to the error detector, which takes the difference between the desired and actual performances, and thereby calculates the error signal

$$e = \theta_i - \theta_0$$

It is this error signal which actually controls the system K and so determines its output. In any given situation, the problem is to design the "black box" K in such a way as to make e go to zero. The reader may easily verify that our thermostat may be put into the form of Fig. 4.1.

A negative feedback system of the type given in Fig. 4.1 is often called a *servomechanism.* Another example of a servomechanism is the steering mechanism of a ship. It is this example which yields the etymology of "cybernetics," for "χυβερνήτηϛ" is Greek for "helmsman." Incidentally, the "governor" on a steam engine, another servomechanism, gets its name from a Latin corruption of the Greek word.

I want to consider now a simple mathematical model of a *linear* servomechanism, where the relation between θ_0 and e is described by a linear integrodifferential equation (with constant coefficients). I give this example only to indicate how mathematics is used to describe feedback systems—the only results of the model I shall use will be qualitative, and they will be "proved" intuitively later on. Consider now a very simple second-order mathematical model of K, as described by the equation† where ζ and ω_n are constants characteristic of K

$$\frac{d^2e}{dt^2} + 2\zeta\omega_n \frac{de}{dt} + \omega_n^2 e = \frac{d^2\theta_i}{dt^2} + 2\zeta\omega_n \frac{d\theta_i}{dt}$$

Let us solve for the error $e(t)$ when our desired performance is a constant velocity output corresponding to $\theta_i(t) = k$. We obtain (see any standard text for the details)

$$e(t) = A + Be^{a_1t} + Ce^{a_2t} \tag{4.1.1}$$

† Quickly derived in any introductory book on servomechanisms.

where A, B, C are constants determined by ω_n, ζ, and the various signal values in K at $t = 0$ (i.e., initially); where the e on the right-hand side is 2.7182818 . . . ; and where a_1 and a_2 are the roots of

$$a^2 + 2\zeta\omega_n a + \omega_n^2 = 0$$

I have considered this second-order linear system not because it possesses any special biological significance, but simply because I want to show a qualitative property of servomechanisms—that of stability. For physical reasons, ζ and ω_n are real numbers, and so a_1 and a_2 are either both real or else conjugate complex numbers. If a_1 and a_2 are both real and negative, then $e^{a_1 t}$ and $e^{a_2 t}$ tend to 0 as t tends to ∞. However, if a_1, say, is positive, then $e^{a_1 t} \to \infty$ as $t \to \infty$, and in this case the system response is unstable. If a_1 and a_2 are conjugate complex numbers $a + ib$ and $a - ib$, then $Be^{a_1 t} + Ce^{a_2 t}$ can be put into the form

$$A + e^{at} (D \cos bt + E \sin bt)$$

which tends to A as $t \to \infty$ if a is negative, but yields unbounded oscillations as $t \to \infty$ if a is positive (Fig. 4.2). Thus, if either a_1 or a_2 has a positive real part, then the error is *unbounded* and the system is *unstable.* But if both a_1 and a_2 have negative real parts, the error is *bounded* and the system is *stable.*

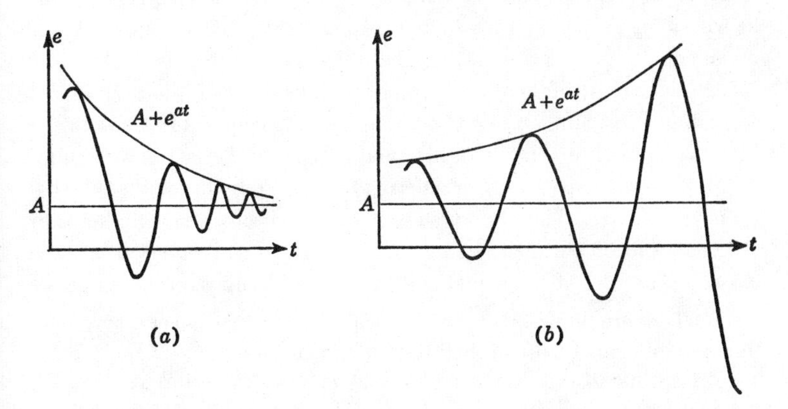

Figure 4.2 Error curves. (*a*) Stable: a negative; (*b*) unstable: a positive.

This result—that a system which is not stable may enter unbounded oscillations†—can also be understood in qualitative terms. Consider again Fig. 4.1, where the purpose of K is to compensate for the error. Now suppose the malfunction of K consists in *overcompensation.* If e is initially positive, K overcompensates, and e becomes negative; K again overcompensates and e becomes large but positive; and so ad infinitum as the system goes into wild oscillations. Our desideratum in constructing a system, of course, is to so design K that the resultant servomechanism is stable, so that the error—given, e.g., by (4.1.1)—soon settles down to its final steady-state value A (hopefully zero).

The insight we have just gained into feedback and oscillation gives us insight into the disease of the nervous system known as ataxia. We quote from Wiener's "Cybernetics":‡

> A patient comes into a neurological clinic. He is not paralyzed, and he can move his legs when he receives the order. Nevertheless, he suffers under a severe disability. He walks with a peculiar uncertain gait, with eyes downcast on the ground and on his legs. He starts each step with a kick, throwing each leg in succession in front of him. If blindfolded, he cannot stand up, and totters to the ground. What is the matter with him?
>
> Another patient comes in. While he sits at rest in his chair, there seems to be nothing wrong with him. However, offer him a cigarette, and he will swing his hand past it in trying to pick it up. This will be followed by an equally futile swing in the other direction, and this by still a third swing back, until his motion becomes nothing but a futile and violent oscillation. Give him a glass of water, and he will empty it in these swings before he is able to bring it to his mouth. What is the matter with him?
>
> Both of these patients are suffering from one form or another of what is known as *ataxia.* Their muscles are strong and healthy enough, but they are unable to organize their actions. The first patient suffers from *tabes dorsalis.* The part of the spinal cord which ordinarily receives sensations

† There are many other ways in which a servomechanism may malfunction, of course, but we shall not go into them here.

‡ Reprinted from "Cybernetics," 2d ed., by Norbert Wiener, p. 95, by permission of The M.I.T. Press, The Massachusetts Institute of Technology, Cambridge, Mass. Copyright 1948 and 1961 by the Massachusetts Institute of Technology.

has been damaged or destroyed by the late sequelae of syphilis. The incoming messages are blunted, if they have not totally disappeared. The receptors in the joints and tendons and muscles and the soles of his feet, which ordinarily convey to him the position and state of motion of his legs, send no messages which his central nervous system can pick up and transmit, and for information concerning his posture he is obliged to trust to his eyes and the balancing organs of his inner ear. In the jargon of the physiologist, he has lost an important part of his proprioceptive or kinesthetic sense.

The second patient has lost none of his proprioceptive sense. His injury is elsewhere, in the cerebellum, and he is suffering from what is known as a cerebellar tremor or purpose tremor. It seems likely that the cerebellum has some function of proportioning the muscular response to the proprioceptive input, and if this proportioning is disturbed, a tremor may be one of the results.

We thus see that for effective action on the outer world it is not only essential that we possess good effectors, but that the performance of these effectors be properly monitored back to the central nervous system, and that the readings of these monitors be properly combined with the other information coming in from the sense organs to produce a properly proportioned output to the effectors.

Thus the first form of ataxia is caused by the loss of feedback, whereas the second seems to be caused by an unstable K.

4.2 Resonant Frequencies in Neural Networks

At this stage, the reader may have become aware of a disturbing discrepancy between our picture of feedback in the nervous system and our picture of the nervous system as a net of formal neurons. We are using feedback of continuously varying quantities in a system which we have modeled with modules operating on a discrete time scale! The resolution of the paradox is to remove the discrete-time-scale assumption from our neural model. We observed that a neuron could not fire more than once every refractory period. However, one may still have any frequency of impulse firings, so long as the period between successive impulses exceeds the refractory period. We might thus code the magnitude of pressure on the sole of the foot, for example, by the frequency of impulse firings along the axons of the appropriate pressure-sensitive nerves. In fact, neurophysiological evidence supports this and indicates that *perhaps* the frequency is proportional to the logarithm of pressure. We can draw an example of frequency coding from our study of the visual system of the frog (Sec. 2.1), where we observed that, for the moving or changing-contrast-detecting ganglion cells, the response is better (more firings, i.e., higher in frequency) when the boundary is sharp or moving fast than when it is blurred or moving slowly.

Such considerations should serve as an antidote to too cavalier an identification of *any* of our neural models with the real brain. For these models only embody a fraction of present-day neurological data, which in itself is only a drop in the ocean of data about the brain awaiting the appropriate experiments.

To heighten the effect of this antidote, we shall devote the remainder of this section to a neural model radically different from the McCulloch-Pitts model—one in which frequencies play a crucial part. It was presented by Peter H. Greene to the 1962 Chicago conference on Self-organizing Systems in a paper entitled "On the Representation of Information by Neural Nets Models." Greene has published fuller accounts of this work in the September and December, 1962, issues of *The Bulletin of Mathematical Biophysics*. He starts by noting that:

> A list of important features of animal behavior related primarily to learning has suggested to many people that an important aspect of brain function is the establishment or modification of functional connections between neural elements. In this paper a considerably more inclusive list of behavioral features suggests that another important aspect may be the utilisation of patterns of activity constituting the resonant responses of linear networks in the brain. To account for the longer list on the basis of connections requires additional assumptions, while both lists follow immediately from the second mechanism. An input locus may become functionally connected to a particular response mode by firing at a frequency which comes to approach the resonant frequency of that mode.

The information in a complicated "cell-assembly" of the type considered could be transmitted through a nerve tract by a very simple frequency code. One neurological guess is that frequency-coded inputs excite the transients in dendritic networks. If the amplitude of the pattern becomes large, as it would near resonance, the all-or-none axonal response would become excited. This axonal response would tend to augment resonant patterns and disrupt other patterns, for a reason inherent in any linear network. It is shown how the mechanism might be related to the list of important behavioral features.

These considerations suggest that a machine for performing skilled actions, instead of being based upon the steady-state response of circuit elements, with various oscillations and instabilities as things to get rid of, *might* instead exploit the oscillations themselves as a vehicle for the action.

Greene then lists nine important features of animal behavior:

1. Behavior is complicated, and involves configurations of many variables (e.g., muscle tensions). Thus, inputs and outputs are often multi-dimensional patterns.

2. The behavior patterns may frequently depend upon the *relative* intensities of their components. Examples might include the direction of movement of an effector controlled by several motor elements, and the behavior patterns like mating in some species which seem to be directed by conflicting drives. Thus, a "response" may correspond to a distribution of ratios of outputs, the absolute values of the outputs determining only the reaction intensity.

3. In conditioning behavior, afferent neurons corresponding to all sorts of stimuli can potentially come to elicit the same output distribution. Thus, response of a neural network may become increasingly invariant to the location of the input.

4. Many responses to stimuli appear to be gradually shaped out of a number of more elementary elements. Examples come from complex behavior studied by ethologists,† as well as all sorts of learning experiments.

5. It is often a complex response as a whole that is set off by a stimulus, not its individual parts independently.

6. A response pattern, once activated, may continue to completion even if the stimulus has been removed.

† Students of instinctive behavior.

7. In the ethological studies, the releasing stimuli tend to be relatively simple and discrete characters. As long as these releasers are present the responses will occur at full intensity, regardless of other seemingly important cues. Effects of releasers in some instances tend to be additive. Intensity of reaction to imperfect stimuli depends only on how much of the releasing stimulus is missing. Likewise, in any first attempt at quantitative learning theory, one makes similar assumptions.

8. If several stimulus components are pooled in activating a response, then the motor centers must be able to respond to this pooled input with integrated, configurational behavior.

9. An animal may often switch from one complete response mode to another without an elaborate process of adjusting all the individual details of the new configuration. This observation is consistent with our impressions of behavior ranging from some simple motor behavior, through complicated instinctual behavior like the display postures of gulls, up to our subjective impressions of our own thoughts.

He then observes that a linear system, describable by a set of differential equations of the form

$$\sum_j b_{ij}\left(\frac{d}{dt}\right) y_j = x_i \qquad i = 1, \ldots, n$$

in which the components x_i and y_j represent the ith input and the jth output, and the $b_{ij}(d/dt)$ are polynomials in the operator d/dt (differentiation with respect to t), has certain well-known properties.

If such a system is excited by a single impulse at an arbitrary point, then its response is well known to be a superposition of *normal modes*, or response distributions, each having a time dependence consisting of a single frequency throughout the network. These *natural frequencies*, or *resonant frequencies*, may be calculated in terms of the network coefficients (b_{ij}). A particular normal mode always consists of a particular distribution of ratios of excitation intensity at the various loci, relative to one another, only the absolute intensity of the whole pattern depending upon the intensity and location of the input. There is no interaction between normal modes, in the sense that excitation of a single normal mode remains confined to that mode. Any pattern of stimulation may be expressed as the sum of sinusoidal oscillations (possibly damped or growing), and each of these input frequencies will excite all the normal modes in amounts dependent upon the frequency and location of the source. If, however, the source frequency approaches a resonant frequency, then the amplitude of the corresponding normal pattern becomes much larger than the amplitudes of the other normal patterns. Thus, exciting the system at any point whatsoever with frequency close to a resonant frequency will predominantly excite a single normal pattern. Hence, at resonance the outputs are large and the response distribution ratios are invariant to the source location.

Greene then proposes a possible model of neural activity based on these properties of linear systems:

Suppose we assume that one of the things which sensory inputs do is to activate linear systems. We naturally expect these systems to be preceded, followed, and controlled by systems *which do not have to be linear, and about which we shall make no assumptions.* As an illustration, we might suppose that inputs activate linear responses in dendritic networks, and that this graded dendritic activity may, if strong enough, excite the all-or-none axonal response. However, our conclusions will depend only upon the properties of linear networks, and not upon the structure of this particular illustrative model. We suppose that the linear networks occur both in sensory and motor mechanisms. The components of the output vectors represent excitation levels at various loci in the network, and these excitations control the activities of the many nerves and muscles that direct the behavior of the animal. We assume that the sensory and motor systems have evolved so that some of the important sensory inputs excite natural modes of neural networks, and that these modes constitute some of the important elements of sensory information, the excitation of which is a condition for the excitation of normal modes of motor networks. The motor modes constitute some of the action patterns in the list of behavioral features.

We shall not here follow Greene's analysis of a specific example in which he shows how one could obtain the different gaits of a "horse" by using the normal modes of a simple neural network.

Instead, we shall content ourselves with quoting the conclusions he draws from this analysis of his model horse:

> In conclusion, I want to emphasize the point of the example of the hypothetical quadruped, with the reminder that these remarks are really intended to apply largely to cell assemblies. Suppose that we found this model animal in our laboratory one day, and, thinking that it was a real animal, we began to perform neurophysiological experiments to learn how its four gaits were controlled. For each gait we would look for a system of neurons that makes the four muscles operate in a prescribed rhythm. For one gait we might expect leg A to be connected to leg B, feedback from which inhibits leg C, while C is connected via a certain number of synaptic delays to D, or some such scheme. Then we would look for a switching element which selects the network which is to control the legs at a particular moment. Perhaps the four systems will not all be physically separate; adjustment of thresholds might enable the same network to perform more than one rhythm. In a complicated network it might be very difficult to identify all the structures and adjustments and to correlate them with the details of overt behavior, but in principle, this is what would constitute fully understanding the nervous system of the animal. *However, in the case of our model animal,* we would not achieve this kind of understanding; and upon the above assumptions, our techniques such as analysis of single cell responses and correlations would only provide us with mountains of unanalyzable and infinitely analyzable data. For, in fact, this model animal has a single system of four neurons and neural paths interconnecting them—not four systems with a selector switch—having no parts which may be interpreted as inhibitory connections, delay units, etc., in analogy to the features of its overt behavior, which when it goes slowly "walks," when it goes faster "trots," when still faster "gallops," etc.

Before concluding this section, we must make two comments spurred by our glance at Greene's paper.

The first point which we make is *not* that the brain is a linear network (in fact, *the more we study the characteristics of the brain, the more horrifyingly nonlinear it seems*), but rather that resonant frequencies in the brain *may* play a vital part in animal behavior—the choice of a *linear* network served to simplify

Greene's mathematical description (which we omitted from our quotations) of the relevant resonant frequencies.†

The second point is vitally important and is brought out by our last quotation. It is that—no matter how objective a physiologist or psychologist may be—his choice of experiment and mode of experimentation is always guided by some hypothesis or model or, simply, hunch. If our model is drastically wrong, we may spend our time making experiments which yield easily misconstrued information or almost no information at all. Mathematical models may be just as wrong as nonmathematical models. One of their beauties is that they often allow logical and numerical predictions and are thus subject to more precise testing than nonmathematical models. But the mere use of formulas gives no magical powers to a theory, and we must always be on the lookout for deficiencies in our old models and for ideas which lead to new models, be they mathematical or not.

4.3 Prosthesis and Homeostasis

The study of feedback in the human nervous system is now beginning to greatly influence the design of artificial limbs.

The oldest type of artificial limb, the peg leg, was designed to replace only one function of the missing limb—that of support. The type of artificial limb used nowadays, such as the artificial arm whose hand can grasp and manipulate objects, restores several degrees of freedom to the wearer. But we saw in Sec. 4.1 the importance of feedback or kinesthetic sense in the full use of our limbs. A task which is receiving much attention now is that of designing artificial limbs with some form of kinesthetic sense—e.g., artificial arms in which the finger tips are fitted with pressure

† The reader who wishes to read more about nerve nets with resonant frequencies should consult R. L. Beurle, Properties of a Mass of Cells Capable of Regenerating Pulses, *Phil. Trans. Roy. Soc. London, Ser. B*, **240:** 55 (1956); and B. G. Farley, Self-organizing Models for Learned Perception, in "Self-organizing Systems," Pergamon Press, New York, 1960.

gauges which can send varying electrical stimuli to the skin of the arm stump of the wearer. In late 1961, a colleague of Wiener reported that Russian scientists had told him that some 35 such feedback-equipped limbs had been made and fitted in the U.S.S.R. The relevant research, both there and in the United States, will require several neurophysiological advances in mapping the kinesthetic feedback pathways into the nervous system, plus theoretical analysis leading to the embodiment of these pathways "in the metal."

There are also important physiological applications of the principle of feedback which are not concerned with the nervous system itself. A great group of cases in which some feedback is not only exemplified in physiological phenomena but is absolutely essential for the continuation of life is found in what is known as *homeostasis*.

Homeostasis is said to be shown by a (physiological) system if, given a moderate disturbance that tends to displace the system from its normal values, its parts so react and interact that the harmful effects of the disturbances are much diminished.

We saw an example of homeostasis in Sec. 3.1. Here are two further examples which should clarify this definition:

a. When a man is chilly, the cooling stimulates a mechanism in the base of the brain that sets him shivering. The muscular activity generates heat which opposes the chilling.

b. Sudden hemorrhage causes a sharp fall in blood pressure. The fall, however, causes the arterioles to constrict, thus lessening the amount of fall.

To what extent the *mathematical theory* of feedback will deepen our understanding of homeostatic mechanisms remains to be seen —certainly the *concept* of feedback is of great help in understanding and categorizing them.†

One aspect of homeostasis is that of self-repair. A Swede, Lars

† For some important relevant papers, see the volume "Homeostatic Mechanisms," Brookhaven Symposia in Biology, no. 10, Upton, N.Y., 1957.

Løfgren, has given a theoretical discussion of networks of logical elements, akin to our formal neurons, which can detect and replace defective elements.†

We shall only summarize his work. He finds that the maximum life-span of a well-localized automaton (i.e., an automaton whose growth, if any, must occur within a fixed volume of space) with unreliable components is obtained if the automaton contains an error-location computation structure. He considers the problem of computing the location of an error in spite of the fact that errors can occur also in the locating parts and finds that the maximum life-span of his variant of a well-localized automaton is finite. It is essentially a quadratic function of the life-span of the components of the automaton. The life-span of the whole automaton can thus be much larger than that of its components.

In his second paper, he relaxes the constraint that the automata be well localized. He finds that a self-repairing non-well-localized automaton can have an unbounded life-span if it grows and repairs itself suitably. In his scheme, such automata contain subautomata which are self-reproducing! He gives a condition which is sufficient for immortality in terms of the error probability, the complexity of the self-reproducing subautomata, and the geometrical form of the whole self-repairing automaton during its expansion.

He also points out that the finite life-spans of the self-repairing well-localized automata can be compared with those of any living plant or animal in nature. The unbounded life-spans of self-repairing non-well-localized automata expanding without finite bound can be compared with the so far unbounded life-span of the population of human beings, regarded as a unit, which at present is expanding on the earth. Løfgren's results would seem to imply that this population would have to expand beyond the terrestrial bound in order to have an unbounded life-span.

† Self-repair as the Limit for Automatic Error-correction, in H. von Foerster and G. Zopf (eds.), "Proc. Symp. on Principles of Self-organization," Pergamon Press, New York, 1962, pp. 181–228; and Kinematic and Tesselation Models of Self-repair, in "Biological Prototypes and Synthetic Systems," Plenum Press, New York, 1962, pp. 342–369.

4.4 Gestalt and Universals

In this section, we will be concerned with material discussed by Wiener in Chap. VI of his "Cybernetics," and in particular with the work of W. H. Pitts and W. S. McCulloch on "How We Know Universals . . . ."†

How do we perceive the identity of the features of a friend whether we see him in three-quarters face or in full-face? How do we recognize a square whether it is large or small, near or far? How do we recognize a circle, even though it is not properly oriented and is seen as an ellipse?

One important factor in the comparison of the form of different objects is the visual-muscular feedback system. Some of this feedback is of a purely homeostatic nature, such as pupil dilation, which keeps light intensity within narrow bounds. When peripheral vision picks up one object conspicuous by brilliancy or color or, above all, by motion, there is a reflex fed back to bring the image into the fovea, that portion of the retina yielding best form and color vision.

Thus we tend to bring any object that attracts our attention into standard position and orientation so that the visual trace of it formed in our nervous system varies within as small a range as possible.

However, this system of visual-muscular feedbacks is not sufficient to completely account for our perception of universals like chairs, circles, etc. We must still account for the way in which our brains enable us to recognize a letter *A*, say, despite its being subjected to many transformations such as rotations, translations on the retina, shifts in perspective, etc. Pitts and McCulloch devoted their paper, cited above, to the discussion of possible neural mechanisms which could account for this perceptive capability of our brains. Their designs show some interesting, though admittedly superficial, similarities to real brain structures.

† How We Know Universals—the Perception of Auditory and Visual Forms, *Bull. Math. Biophys.*, **9**: 124–147 (1947). Quoted by permission of The University of Chicago Press.

We are now going to indulge in a little mathematics. To this end, we recall the concept of a group:

Definition 4.4.1 A *group of transformations* is a collection G of transformations such that if A and B are in G, then so also is AB in G (where AB is the transformation obtained by first carrying out B and *then* the transformation A; note that, in general, $AB \neq BA$); and where:

a. I, the identity transformation, is in G. (I is the trivial "transformation" that leaves everything fixed, e.g., a translation through zero distance.)
b. If A is in G, then it has an inverse A^{-1} in G, where $AA^{-1} = A^{-1}A = I$. (A^{-1} is the transformation whose effect is precisely the opposite of that of A.)

Note that for transformation we automatically have associativity:

$$(AB)C = A(BC)$$
$$= C \text{ followed by } B \text{ followed by } A$$

Pitts and McCulloch point out that

. . . numerous nets, embodied in special nervous structures, serve to classify information according to useful common characters. In vision they detect the equivalence of apparitions related by similarity and congruence like those of a single physical thing seen from various places. In audition, they recognise timbre and chord, regardless of pitch. The equivalent apparitions in all cases share a common figure and define a group of transformations that takes the equivalents into one another but preserve the figures invariant. So, for example, the group of translations removes a square appearing at one place to other places; but the figure of a square it leaves invariant. These figures are the "geometric objects" of Cartan and Weyl, and the "Gestalten" of Wertheimer and Kohler.

We seek general methods for designing nervous nets which recognise figures in such a way as to produce the same output for every input belonging to the figure.

Now the things we see or hear are mapped within the brain as patterns of neuron firing in a cortical manifold (i.e., body of cells in the cortex) M. The distribution of excitation in M is described by a function $\phi(x,t)$, where $\phi(x,t) = 1$ if there is a neuron at position x firing at time t, and $\phi(x,t) = 0$ otherwise.

Let G be the group of transformations which carry the functions $\phi(x,t)$ describing apparitions into their equivalents of the same figure and suppose G has N members.

Pitts and McCulloch consider the case where the transformations T of G can be generated by transformations $\tilde{T}$ in the underlying manifold M, so that†

$$T\phi(x) = \phi(\tilde{T}x)$$

For example, if G is the group of translations, then

$$T\phi(X) = \phi(x + a_T)$$

where a_T is a constant vector depending only upon T. If G is the group of dilations

$$T\phi(x) = \phi(a_T x)$$

where a_T is a positive real number depending only upon T. All such transformations are linear, that is

$$\begin{aligned} T(a\phi(x) + b\psi(x)) &= a\phi(\tilde{T}x) + b\psi(\tilde{T}x) \\ &= aT\phi(x) + bT\psi(x) \end{aligned}$$

The simplest way to construct invariants of a given distribution $\phi(x,t)$ of excitation is to average over the group G. So let f be an arbitrary functional (i.e., a function of a function) which assigns a number to each $\phi(x,t)$. We form every transfer $T\phi$ of $\phi(x,t)$, evaluate $f(T\phi)$, and average the results over G to obtain

$$a = \frac{1}{N} \sum_{\substack{\text{all} \\ T \varepsilon G}} f(T\phi)$$

If we had started with $S\phi$, S in G, instead of ϕ, we would have

† Where there is no risk of confusion, we omit the time variable and write $\phi(x,t)$ simply as $\phi(x)$.

$$\frac{1}{N}\sum_{\substack{\text{all}\\ T\varepsilon G}} f(TS\phi) = \frac{1}{N}\sum_{\substack{\text{all}\\ R\varepsilon G\\ \text{such}\\ \text{that}\\ RS^{-1}\varepsilon G}} f(R\phi)$$

$$= a, \text{ since } G \text{ is a group}$$

To characterize completely the figure of $\phi(x,t)$ under G (i.e., the universal corresponding to the apparition which produces the neuronal firing pattern $\phi(x,t)$), we need a whole collection of such numbers a for different functionals f (one functional corresponding to "circularity," one to "squareness," etc.). We can distinguish between the different functionals by indexing them with a subscript ξ to yield f_ξ and letting ξ range over a set Ξ. We thus obtain the various averages

$$f_\xi(\phi) = \frac{1}{N}\sum_{T\varepsilon G} f_\xi(T\phi)$$

We shall actually introduce a new manifold of neurons, again called Ξ, with one neuron for each ξ. Ξ may split into several dimensions, in which case we can specify ξ by its coordinates $(\xi_1, \ldots, \xi_m)$. If the neuron system needs less than complete information in order to recognize shapes, the manifold Ξ may be much smaller than M, have fewer dimensions, and indeed reduce to isolated points. The time t and some of the x_j representing position in M may serve as coordinates in Ξ.

Suppose the dimensions of Ξ are all spatial. Then the simplest neural net to realize the above formal process is obtained in the following way: Let the original manifold M be duplicated on $N - 1$ sheets, a manifold M_T for each T of G, and connected to M or its sensory afferents in such a way that whatever produces the distribution $\phi(x)$ on M produces the transformed distribution $T\phi(x)$ on M_T. Thereupon separately for each value of ξ for each M_T, the value of $f_\xi(T\phi)$ is computed by a suitable net, and the results from all the M_T's are added by convergence on the neuron at the point ξ of the mosaic Ξ.

But to proceed entirely in this way usually requires far, far too many associative neurons to be plausible. The manifolds M_T together possess the sum of the dimensions of M and the degrees of freedom of the group G. More important is the number of neurons and fibers necessary to compute the values of $f_\xi(T\phi)$ which depends, in principle, upon the entire distribution $T\phi$ and therefore requires a separate computer for every ξ, for every T of G. This difficulty is most acute if f_ξ is computed in a structure separated from the M_T, since in that case all operations must be performed by relatively few long fibers.

We can improve matters considerably by the following device:

Let the manifolds M_T be connected as before, but raise their thresholds so that their specific afferents alone are no longer able to excite them. Now let us introduce additional fibers ramifying throughout each M_T, so that when active they remedy the deficiency in summation and permit M_T to display $T\phi(x)$ as before.

Let all the neurons with the same coordinate x on the N different M_T's send axons to the neuron at x on another sheet exactly like them, say Q, and suppose any one of them can excite this neuron. If the additional fibers introduced above are excited in a regular cycle so that every one of the sheets M_T in turn, and only one at a time, receives the increment of summation it requires for activity, then all of the transforms $T\phi$ of $\phi(x)$ will be displayed successively on Q (cf. Fig. 4.3).

A single f_ξ computer for each ξ, taking its input from Q instead of from the M_T's, will now suffice to produce all the values of $f_\xi(T\phi)$ in turn as the "time scanning" presents all the $T\phi$'s on Q in the course of a cycle. These values of $f_\xi(T\phi)$ may be accumulated through a cycle at the final Ξ-neuron ξ in any way.

This device illustrates a useful general principle which we may call the *exchangeability of time and space*. This states that any dimension or degree of freedom of a manifold or group can be exchanged freely with as much delay in the operation as corresponds to the number of distinct places along that dimension.

To the best of my knowledge, it has not been possible to prove neurophysiologically that the mechanisms presented above are

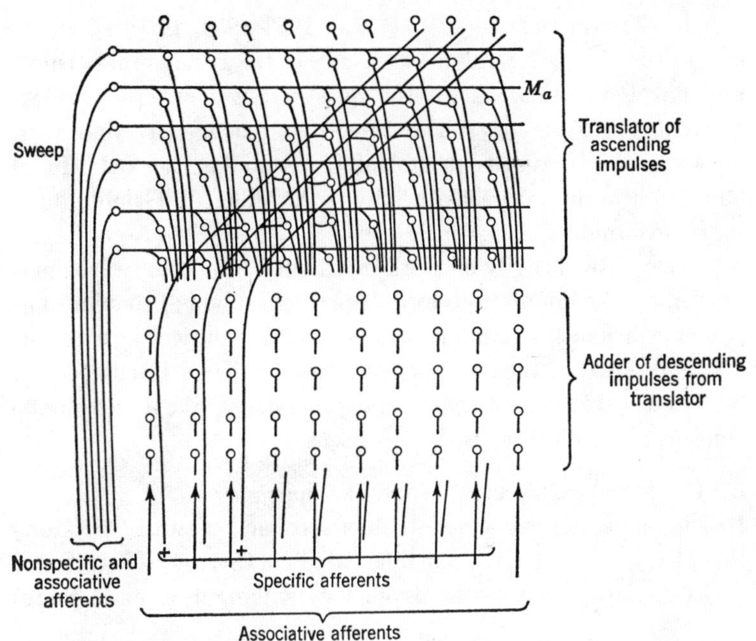

Figure 4.3 Impulses enter slantwise along the specific afferents, marked by plusses, and ascend until they reach the level M_a in the columns of the receptive layer activated at the moment by the nonspecific afferents. These provide summation adequate to permit the impulses to enter that level but no other.

actually employed in the human brain. However, the superficial resemblances are so great that Wiener was able to recount that when the neurophysiologist von Bonin saw a diagram like our Fig. 4.3, he asked: "Is this a diagram of the fourth layer of the visual cortex?"

4.5 Some Further Topics

This section is devoted to a brief discussion of topics, primarily those of cybernetic psychology and artificial intelligence, which we shall not discuss in detail in this book.

In the American academic year 1958–1959, three scientists met at the Center for Advanced Study in the Behavioral Sciences and devoted themselves to the question: Are cybernetic ideas relevant to psychology? The interested reader may find their answer in the affirmative delightfully presented in the book "Plans and the Structure of Behavior," by G. A. Miller, E. Galanter, and K. H. Pribram.†

They draw heavily on work in artificial intelligence—the programming of computers to exhibit problem-solving behavior. The reader will find his best introduction to this subject in a review article by M. L. Minsky, "Steps Toward Artificial Intelligence."‡

In constructing a cybernetic psychology, the fundamental concept of feedback is used in two senses:

a. The literal sense, as in a servomechanism
b. The metaphorical sense—that of feedback between the study of the brain and of the machine (which in this case is manifested as the feedback between psychology and artificial intelligence)

For the details of the literal use of feedback, we refer you to the above book. Here we shall briefly discuss the metaphorical feedback between the study of brains and the study of computers. This can take the form of a *neurophysiological* discussion such as that accompanying our study of the McCulloch and Pitts brain model, but in this section our interest is in the use of computers as automata to illustrate the operation of various *psychological* theories. Turing's work (cf. our discussion in Sec. 1.6 of Turing's hypothesis) indicates that a computer-like mechanism is the right kind of machine on which to simulate human behavior. We note that the computer's task is not a complete simulation (we do not require a computer which plays chess to have fingers), but merely a simulation of those aspects of behavior under study at the time. Thus a psychological theorist may avail himself of our metaphorical feedback by embodying his ideas in a program of instructions to be stored in the "memory" of the computer—when

† Published by Holt, Rinehart and Winston, Inc., New York, 1960.
‡ *Proc. IRE*, 49 (1): 8–30 (1961).

"stimuli" are presented to the computer it will, like an organism, operate upon the input according to its program in order to generate a "response."

We want to point up the distinction *artificial intelligence versus simulation*, between making a computer solve a problem anyhow and making it solve the problem in a manner paralleling that in which a human would. Minsky remarks that

> . . . it seems certain that, for at least a few years, there will be a close association between theories of human behavior and attempts to increase the intellectual capacity of machines. But in the long run, we must be prepared to discover profitable lines of programming which do not deliberately imitate human behavior.

But the fact remains that what is needed by the *psychologist* is an attempt to simulate the human chess player or logician, not just to replace him or defeat him.

To give the reader a small taste of computer programs written in the study of *artificial intelligence*, we briefly mention two such programs:

H. Gelernter and N. Rochester† programmed a computer to prove theorems in plane geometry by applying given rules of inference to a given set of axioms. They equipped the machine to inspect diagrams much as a student does—for the truth of a proposition can be supposed with great reliability by measuring a few drawings (using several to avoid being trapped by some accidental property of any one figure). The diagrams simplify tremendously the process of searching for a proof.

A. L. Samuel‡ summarizes his research as follows:

> Two machine-learning procedures have been investigated in some detail using the game of checkers. Enough work has been done to verify

† Intelligent Behavior in Problem-solving Machines, *IBM J. Res. Develop.*, **2:** 336 ff. (1958).

‡ Some Studies in Machine Learning, Using the Game of Checkers, *IBM J. Res. Develop.*, **3:** 210–229 (1959).

the fact that a computer can be programmed so that it will learn to play a better game of checkers than can be played by the person who wrote the program. Furthermore, it can learn to do this in a remarkably short period of time (8 or 10 hours of machine-playing time) when given only the rules of the game, a sense of direction, and a redundant and incomplete list of parameters which are thought to have something to do with the game, but whose correct signs and relative weights are unknown and unspecified. The principles of machine learning verified by these experiments are, of course, applicable to many other situations.

Let me briefly retrace the thread of this chapter and point out to the reader several interesting problems which serve as a challenge for future research. We saw the fundamental importance of feedback and how this concept could give us insight into certain nervous diseases, into homeostasis, and help us in the design of more effective prosthetics. These three areas all require much further research. We saw the need for more sophisticated neural models to accommodate feedback mechanisms and frequency coding of sensory information. We saw that visual-muscular feedback plays a part in our recognition of visual forms and looked at a suggested neural network to supplement this feedback. However, we are still a long long way from understanding the neural networks underlying our perception of universals. The exploration of the literal and metaphorical uses of feedback in psychology and the related computer programming art of artificial intelligence certainly afford many research problems.

Topics of great interest which we can only mention here are those of self-reproducing automata, molecular automata theory, genetic coding, and Chomsky's mathematical linguistics. The reader who wishes to find material on such topics should browse through such journals as *The Bulletin of Mathematical Biophysics*, *Information and Control*, *Journal of the Association for Computing Machinery*, *Journal of Theoretical Biology*, and *Kybernetik*, as well as the proceedings of the professional groups of the IRE (IEEE) on electronic computers, information theory, etc. A book discussing feedback *within* living cells is B. C. Goodwin, "Temporal Organisation in Cells," Academic Press, Inc., London, 1963.

We conclude this chapter with the realization that cybernetics has many, many exciting problems ahead of it. Perhaps the most outstanding problem in which cybernetic methods can supplement research in psychology and physiology is the provision of an understanding—which we lack at present—of what the overall coordinating and integrating principles are which interrelate the activities of the various subsystems which constitute the human nervous system.

5

Gödel's Incompleteness Theorem

In this, our final chapter, we shift our center of interest first to the foundations of mathematics. In Sec. 5.1, we shall give a brief historical review of the formalist approach to the foundations of mathematics and see how Gödel's theorem invalidated much of the Formalist program. In Sec. 5.2, we shall revise the concepts of recursive sets which we studied in Chap. 1; in Sec. 5.3, we shall discuss some general properties of recursive logics; in Sec. 5.4, we shall restrict ourselves to arithmetical logics, yielding a proof of Gödel's Incompleteness Theorem, in Sec. 5.5. Finally, we shall return to the main theme of this book by discussing the philosophical controversy centering around the implications of Gödel's theorem for the question: Are brains essentially superior to machines? My desire to prove Gödel's theorem is thus essentially threefold: first, because of its implications for the brain-machine controversy; second, because of its importance in the foundations of mathematics; and third, because I believe the proof given in this book is sufficiently short and simple to help dispel the myth—an integral part of the modern folklore of mathematics—that the proof of Gödel's theorem is necessarily so recondite as to be accessible only to the specialist in mathematical logic.

5.1 The Foundations of Mathematics†

The philosopher Kant proclaimed that the axioms of Euclidean geometry were given a priori to human intuition. This proclamation was in the spirit of the definition of an axiom of a logical system such as Euclidean geometry as a self-evident truth, a definition that had stood unquestioned for 2,000 years.

This whole attitude received a severe jolt in the nineteenth century from the work of Bolyai, Lobachewsky, and Riemann. They postulated systems of geometry that were non-Euclidean—more specifically, systems which denied the truth of the following *axiom* of the Euclidean scheme: "Given a line, and a point not on it, then there exists precisely one line through the given point parallel to the given line." And we now live in an age in which the accepted view of the universe afforded us by the Einsteinean theory of relativity involves a space whose geometry is best described by a Riemannian non-Euclidean scheme in which parallel lines just do not exist.

In other words, our present view not only contradicts Kant's view that the Euclidean axioms are given a priori to human intuition, it even asserts that one of Euclid's axioms, the so-called parallel axiom, is actually untrue as a description of the universe. We now believe that Euclidean geometry is quite accurate enough to describe the spatial relations of our everyday lives, but not the spatial entirety of our universe. As a result, however, we are now

† For a fuller and very readable introduction to this subject, see Ernest Nagel and James R. Newman, "Gödel's Proof," New York University Press, New York, 1958. For a thoroughgoing technical treatment, see E. W. Beth, "The Foundations of Mathematics," North Holland Publishing Company, Amsterdam, 1959.

faced with a genuine and important question which the Kantian viewpoint allowed us to dispose of effortlessly: How do we know that Euclidean geometry is consistent (i.e., free from contradictions)?

Just to aggravate the enormity of this question, *Riemann showed that if Euclidean geometry was consistent, then his non-Euclidean geometry was consistent.* Here was a fine contretemps—not only had the consistency of the Euclidean scheme ceased to be a priori evident, but it was shown that its consistency implied that of a rival scheme! One evident conclusion was that the students of axiomatic systems had to tackle the problem of consistency quite independently of any questions as to whether or not the system afforded an apparently "true" description of the "real world."

Meanwhile, developments in set theory were showing that the consistency of a system could not be checked by mere common sense. In fact, the system of set theory propounded by Cantor seemed completely consistent until Russell, among others, pointed out that this apparently "safe" system contained an annihilating paradox, which runs as follows: Consider the set of mathematicians—it is not a mathematician, and so this set does not belong to itself. However, the set of things talked about in this chapter is talked about in this chapter, so this set does belong to itself. Hence we may define N to be the set of all those sets which do not belong to themselves. Thus

M belongs to N if and only if M does not belong to M

So the set of mathematicians belongs to N, but the set of things described in this chapter does not. Does N belong to N? According to the above

N belongs to N if and only if N does not belong to N

A paradox! And so naïve set theory is inconsistent. Now Russell avoided such contradictions by introducing his Theory of Types, but the point here is that consistency is not an evident property of a logical system.

Riemann had shown that his geometry is consistent if Euclidean geometry is consistent, and Hilbert showed that Euclidean geometry is consistent if arithmetic—the elementary theory of the positive whole numbers—is consistent. The problem was thus to exhibit a consistent axiomatic system of arithmetic.

Now, a logical system has a collection of axioms from which we obtain theorems by the repeated application of a number of rules of inference. The school of Formalists, led by Hilbert, decided that in their search for proofs of consistency they would ignore all questions of the truth and meaning of the axioms and theorems and would instead regard the axioms as mere strings of symbols and the rules of inference as just methods of obtaining new strings. They further decided to require that the rules of inference operate in a purely finite well-determined manner, such as is exemplified very well in the operation of the Turing machines we studied in Chap. 1. Let us then agree to call a logical system satisfying such conditions a *recursive logic*. If we wish to use a recursive logic to describe the theory of positive integers, we must equip it with symbols which correspond to the basic quantitative notions of elementary number theory.

The Formalists were searching for a consistent arithmetical logic which was *complete*, i.e., in which one could prove as theorems all true statements about the integers. Further, they demanded that the consistency of the system be shown in a manner as safe, well determined, and "finitistic" as that in which the rules of inference were to operate.

This Formalist program was wrecked by Gödel's Incompleteness Theorem, first expounded in his famous paper on formally undecidable theorems of Principia Mathematica and related systems.†

His theorem states that *any* adequate consistent arithmetical logic is incomplete, i.e., there exist true statements about the

† Kurt Gödel, Uber formal unentscheidbare Sätze der Principia Mathematica und verwandter Systeme, I (Part II has not appeared), *Monats. Math. Phys.*, **38:** 173–198 (1931). This is now available in an English translation; see Kurt Gödel, "On Formally Undecidable Propositions of Principia Mathematica and Related Systems," translated by B. Meltzer, with an introduction by R. B. Braithwaite, Basic Books, Inc., Publishers, New York.

integers which cannot be proved within such a logic. This important result (which we shall prove in the sequel) showed that the Formalist search for a complete consistent arithmetical logic was doomed to failure. Actually, Gödel showed even more—namely, that it was impossible to show that an arithmetical logic (admittedly incomplete) was consistent by methods *which could be represented in the logic itself.*

Gentzen has since proved elementary number theory consistent but by using "ϵ_0-induction," which is an infinite extension of the familiar technique of mathematical induction—a method not satisfactory to the Formalists because it is not "finitistic." The present situation as regards the search for a consistency proof for arithmetic is thus as follows: Gödel has shown that there exists no finitistic proof expressible within arithmetic itself; Gentzen has given a proof, but only by using methods whose consistency is perhaps as open to doubt as that of the system they were called in to justify; and the question of whether or not there exists a consistency proof not expressible within arithmetic but nevertheless "finitistic" is still open.

5.2 Revision on Recursion

My treatment of logics and Gödel's theorem in Secs. 5.3 to 5.5 is a motivated informal treatment based on the unmotivated formal treatment given in Chap. 8 of Martin Davis's "Computability and Unsolvability."† I have tried to emulate the admirable style of Emil L. Post in his lucid paper "Recursively Enumerable Sets and Their Decision Problems."‡

Let me repeat the assurance I gave in Sec. 1.6:

> My presentation will be rigorous, save that, where it is intuitively evident that a procedure is effective, I shall take it as proven that a suitable Turing machine exists. You may rest assured that in every case a rigorous proof exists—I refer you to Davis's book.

† McGraw-Hill Book Company, Inc., New York, 1958.

‡ *Bull. Am. Math. Soc.*, **50:** 284–316 (1944).

It was in this vein that we were led to make the following definitions in our intuitive language of effective procedures:

Definition 1.6.1 A *function* is called *recursive* if there exists an effective procedure for computing it.

Definition 1.6.2 A *set* is *recursive* if there exists an effective procedure for telling whether or not an element belongs to it.

Definition 1.6.3 A *set* is *recursively enumerable* if there exists an effective procedure for generating its elements, one after another.

If I want to convince a computer user that a program exists—without consideration for time or storage limitations—then I show him the flow diagrams, not the program in machine language. The proofs I give, then, are related to the rigorous proofs, as the flow diagrams are related to the machine language programs. I hope to show all the essentials, merely omitting finicky details which serve only to obscure initial understanding.

We proved three theorems on recursive and recursively enumerable sets.

Theorem 1.6.1 If R and S are recursively enumerable sets, then so are $R \cup S$ and $R \cap S$.

Theorem 1.6.2 A set S of positive integers is recursive if and only if both S and $\overline{S}$ are recursively enumerable.

Theorem 1.6.3 There exists a recursively enumerable set of positive integers which is not recursive.

The last theorem really constitutes an abstract form of Gödel's theorem. The hard work in the next two sections will be to define and understand the concept of an adequate ω-consistent arithmetical logic. It will then be an easy task to prove Gödel's Incompleteness Theorem: "Every adequate ω-consistent arithmetical logic is incomplete."

5.3 Recursive Logics

We now wish to formulate in very broad terms what the Formalists require of a logic. First we must have an alphabet $a_0, a_1, a_2, \ldots$ in terms of which we can write the statements of our logic. A finite sequence of these symbols will be called a "word."† The result of juxtaposing the pair of words X, Y will be written XY.

By a *statement*, we mean something which asserts a proposition that is either true or false. By a *predicate*, on the other hand, we mean an expression that contains certain symbols and becomes a statement when these symbols are replaced by any members of a specified set. If the specified set is a set of words, we may speak of a *word predicate*. Such a predicate is called *recursive* if there is an effective procedure for telling whether the statements, obtained from the predicate by replacement of the variables, are true or false.

For example, "x is a man" is a word predicate, and if we replace x by the word "John" we get the true statement "John is a man," whereas if we replace x by the word "chair" we get the false statement "Chair is a man." Our example is a *singulary* predicate in that it contains only a *single* variable.

For our recursive logic, we demand an effective procedure for telling whether or not a word is an axiom and we demand an effective procedure for telling us whether or not a rule of inference allows us to deduce one word from several others.‡ We can state this precisely in the following definition:

Definition 5.3.1 By a *recursive logic L*, we mean a recursive set of words, called the *axioms* of L, together with a finite set of recursive word predicates, none of which is singular, called the *rules of inference* of L.

† Note that our use of "word" is somewhat unusual. In this terminology, a phrase such as "Cogito cogito ergo cogito sum" would be a word on an alphabet which includes "the blank" as a letter!

‡ For a comparison of different ways of assuring this effectiveness, see M. A. Arbib, Monogenic Normal Systems Are Universal, *J. Australian Math. Soc.*, 3: 3 (1963).

When $R(Y,X_1, \ldots, X_n)$ is a rule of inference of L, we shall sometimes say that Y is a *consequence* of $X_1, \ldots, X_n$, by R, in L.

A finite sequence of words $X_1, X_2, \ldots, X_n$ is called a *proof* (of X_n) in a logic L if, for each i, $1 \leq i \leq n$, either X_i is an axiom, or there exist $j, \ldots, k < i$, such that X_i is a consequence of $X_j, \ldots, X_k$ in L by one of the rules of inference of L. Each of the X_i, $i = 1, 2, \ldots, n$, is called a *step* of the proof. We say that W is a *theorem* of L or that W is *provable* in L and we write

$$Th(L): W$$

if there is a proof of W in L.

The reader will find an example of such a proof in our proof of Lemma 5.4.1 in the next section.

We write T_L for the set of theorems of L. Note that every axiom of L is a theorem of L.

Theorem 5.3.1 T_L is recursively enumerable.

Proof We have to provide an effective method of generating all the theorems of L. Since the axioms form a recursive set, we may effectively enumerate them as $A_1, A_2, A_3, \ldots$. For each natural number n, the reader may verify that the proofs with at most n steps which use only axioms from the collection $\{A_1,A_2, \ldots, A_n\}$ form a recursively enumerable set. The theorems which are last steps of such proofs then also form a recursively enumerable set. Our result easily follows. Q.E.D.

If in our logic L we want to talk about a set Q of natural numbers, we must have for each n an effective method of writing down a word W_n which means $n \varepsilon Q$. We may regard L as furnishing a "semicomplete" description of Q if we can prove W_n to be a theorem of L precisely when $n \varepsilon Q$. The description of Q is "complete" if we also have statements $\overline{W}_n$, to be interpreted as $n \not\varepsilon Q$, such that we can prove $\overline{W}_n$ to be a theorem of L precisely when

$n \notin Q$. In other words, L furnishes a complete description of Q, when we can prove in L for each n whether or not n belongs to Q. This motivates our next definition:

Definition 5.3.2 A logic L is said to be *semicomplete* wrt (with respect to) a set of integers Q, if there exists a recursively enumerable set of words $W_0, W_1, W_2, \ldots$ such that

$$Q = \{n \mid Th(L): W_n\}$$

L is said to be *complete* wrt Q if it is semicomplete wrt both Q and $\bar{Q}$.

Theorem 5.3.2 If L is semicomplete wrt Q, then Q is recursively enumerable.

Proof $Q = \{n \mid T_L \cap \{W_0, W_1, W_2 \ldots\}\}$ is obtained effectively from the intersection of two recursively enumerable sets and so is recursively enumerable by Theorem 1.6.1. Q.E.D.

Bearing in mind Theorem 1.6.2, we now obtain:

Corollary 5.3.3 If Q is recursively enumerable but not recursive, then no recursive logic is complete wrt Q.

With this corollary, we are well on our way to Gödel's theorem, for it implies that if we try to develop the theory of numbers within a recursive logic L to the point where membership in a given set Q of integers can be adequately dealt with (i.e., so that a given number n belongs to Q if and only if some effectively corresponding word is provable in L), then this is possible only if Q happens to be at least recursively enumerable. Hence, nonrecursively enumerable sets can at best be dealt with only in an incomplete manner within a recursive logic.

To point up the interest to automata theorists of sets which are *not* recursively enumerable, we briefly detour from our progress toward Gödel's theorem to discuss the *halting problem for Turing machines*. Recall (see Sec. 1.5) that if we place a Turing machine in its initial stage q_0 and present it with a tape $\bar{n}$, it will start scanning, printing, and moving the tape—but we have no guarantee that it will stop. (Think of a Turing machine which does nothing but move right.) The halting problem for a Turing machine Z is to determine, for each and every number n, whether or not Z will ever stop computing after being started in state q_0 scanning the leftmost square of the tape $\bar{n}$. The halting problem is said to be *solvable* if there exists an *effective method* for carrying out the desired determination. If $\bar{R}_Z$ is the set of numbers n for which Z does *not* stop computing, then the question "Is the halting problem solvable for Z?" is equivalent to the question "Is $\bar{R}_Z$ recursive?" Certainly, $\bar{R}_Z$ is of interest to automata theorists. Yet we shall see that there exist Turing machines Z for which the halting problem is not effectively solvable and for which $\bar{R}_Z$ is not even recursively enumerable.

Now, R_Z (the set of numbers n for which Z *does* stop computing) is *always* recursively enumerable: at stage

$$n(n = 1,2,3, \ldots)$$

we simply emit into R_Z those among the first n integers for which Z stops computing on the corresponding tapes within n steps. So, if $\bar{R}_Z$ is not recursive, then R_Z is not recursive, but is still recursively enumerable, so that $\bar{R}_Z$ is not recursively enumerable (cf. Theorem 1.6.2). Hence, to find a Z for which $\bar{R}_Z$ is not recursively enumerable, we have to find a Z for which R_Z is not recursive. But this is immediate (by Theorem 1.6.3) if we can show that every recursively enumerable set is an R_Z for some Turing machine Z. This is easy for, using Turing's hypothesis (recall Sec. 1.6), we know that given a recursively enumerable set R, we can find a Turing machine $Z(R)$ which embodies the following effective procedure:

Given a number n, generate successive members $x_1, x_2, \ldots$ of R until an x_i is found which equals n. Emit n. Stop.

Clearly $Z(R)$ only halts if n is in R; i.e., $R = R_{Z(R)}$.

Thus if R is recursively enumerable but not recursive, $\bar{R}_{Z(R)} = \bar{R}$ is not recursively enumerable, and $Z(R)$ has an unsolvable halting problem.

Thus there are sets which are not recursively enumerable, yet are nonetheless of great interest for automata theorists. Hence we have already found a degree of incompleteness in our recursive logic.

5.4 Arithmetical Logics

This section is devoted to the motivation and definition of all the concepts contained in the statement of Gödel's Incompleteness Theorem: "Every ω-consistent and adequate arithmetical logic is incomplete."

A recursive logic L is called an *arithmetical logic* if it has the properties listed below under headings 1, 2, 3, and 4. Each of these four sections is divided into two subsections—(**a**) gives an informal motivational discussion, while (**b**) gives the formal requirements so motivated.

1 Well-formed Formulas†

a. We must have an effective way of telling whether or not a string of symbols is meaningful, irrespective of its truth or falsity. The concept of a well-formed formula (wff) in a logic is akin to that of a grammatically correct sentence in English. In the intended interpretation of the logic, the wff's include the words that represent sentences or predicates. In this vein, "x is a man" and "Socrates was a man" are both wff's in English, whereas "Man not" is not a wff of English.

b. For each arithmetical logic L, there is a recursive non-empty set of words called the wff's of L. All theorems of L are wff's.

2 Propositional Connectives

a. Given wff's A and B in a logic, we wish to be able to combine them in various ways to obtain new wff's, such as:

† Abbreviation: wff.

$\sim A$	not A
$A \supset B$	A implies B
$A \,\&\, B$	A and B
$A \vee B$	A or B (or both)
$A \equiv B$	A if and only if B

The logics we consider are *two-valued* logics, i.e., any *statement* is true or false (a *predicate* only assumes a truth value upon substitution of constants for all its variables). We may regard the *propositional connectives* given above as two-valued functions (cf. Boolean functions, Sec. 3.1), e.g., $A \,\&\, B$ is true when A is true and B is true; and $A \,\&\, B$ is false otherwise.

We can express this in a "truth table," which tabulates the truth value of $A \,\&\, B$, given the truth values of A and of B.†

A	B	$A \,\&\, B$
T	T	T
T	F	F
F	T	F
F	F	F

We require $A \supset B$ to be true whenever both A is true and B is true. We also require that if A is true and $A \supset B$ is true, then we can infer that B is true. One scheme of assigning truth values to $A \supset B$ consistent with these requirements is as follows:

A	B	$A \supset B$
T	T	T
T	F	F
F	T	T
F	F	T

We also have the following:

† See, e.g., W. V. O. Quine, "Mathematical Logic," rev. ed., Harvard University Press, Cambridge, Mass., 1958.

A	$\sim A$
T	F
F	T

and

A	B	$A \vee B$	$A \equiv B$
T	T	T	T
T	F	T	F
F	T	T	F
F	F	F	T

Now we can check that all our propositional connectives can be built up from $\sim$ and $\supset$:

$$A \,\&\, B = \sim[A \supset \sim B]$$

$$A \vee B = \sim A \supset B$$

$$A \equiv B = [A \supset B] \,\&\, [B \supset A] = \sim[[A \supset B] \supset \sim[B \supset A]]$$

Hence if we only introduce the connectives $\sim$ and $\supset$ and ensure that they behave properly by suitable axioms, our logic will be suitably equipped with propositional connectives. We must, of course, require that these connectives preserve well-formedness.

b. There are recursive word functions $[A \supset B]$ of A and B, and $\sim A$ of A. $\sim A$ is a wff if and only if A is a wff. $[A \supset B]$ is a wff if and only if A and B are both wff's. If A, B, and C are wff's of L, then we have the following axioms:

$$Th(L)\colon [A \supset [B \supset A]] \qquad (5.4.1)$$

$$Th(L)\colon [[A \supset [B \supset C]] \supset [[A \supset B] \supset [A \supset C]]]$$

$$Th(L)\colon [[\sim B \supset \sim A] \supset [A \supset B]] \qquad (5.4.2)$$

Moreover, we introduce the rule of inference:

If $Th(L)\colon A$ and $Th(L)\colon [A \supset B]$ then $Th(L)\colon B$

This rule is called *modus ponens.*

3 *Quantifiers*

a. In setting up the theory of numbers, we must have at our disposal numerical variables. We thus introduce a sequence $x_1, x_2, x_3, \ldots$ of variables, each able to assume values which include the natural numbers.

Given a wff A, we wish to be able to assert that it holds for *all* possible values of one of its variables x_1, say, or that it holds for *at least one* value of a variable. We thus want:

Universal quantification: $(x_1)\ A$: A is true for all values of x_1
Existential quantification: $(\exists x_1)A$: There exists at least one value of x_1 for which A is true

If a variable in a wff is quantified by a universal or existential quantifier, we say that it is *bound.* Otherwise, we say that the variable is *free.* For example, x is bound in the (true) statement $(x)[x + 2 > x]$, but is free in the predicate $[x + 2 > x]$ & $(y)[y > 0]$. We thus introduce $B(M,A)$, to be read "M is bound in A." We say a wff is *closed* if no variable is free in it. Thus, in the intended interpretation, closed wff's represent sentences, whereas predicates are represented by wff's that are not closed. If we have a predicate, we may form a sentence from it by universal quantification over all its free variables. Thus $[x > y]$ yields the (false) sentence $(x)(y)[x > y]$. The closed wff $C(W)$ obtained from a given wff W is called the *closure of W*. Further, if X is a wff and M is a variable free in X, we wish to be able to make *substitutions* and so denote by $S(X,M,N)$ the word that results on replacing the variable M by N at all of M's occurrences in X.

b. There is a recursively enumerable sequence $x_1, x_2, x_3, \ldots$ of distinct words of L called *variables.* No variable is a wff.

There is a recursive binary word function $(M)A$. $(M)A$ is a wff if and only if A is a wff and M is a variable. By $(\exists M)A$, we understand $\sim(M) \sim A$.

There is a recursive binary word predicate $B(M,A)$. If $B(M,A)$ is true, then A is a wff, M is a variable, and M is a part of A (i.e., $A = BMC$ for suitable B and C). When $B(x_1,A)$ is true, we say that x_1 is *bound* in A. When $B(x_1,A)$ is false and x_1 is a part of A, we say that x_1 is *free* in A.

If no variable is free in any wff B that is a part of the wff A, then A is said to be *closed.* We write *cwff* for closed wff.

$B(x_i,(x_i)A)$ is always true.

If $B(x_i,A)$, and A is a part of the wff C, then $B(x_i,C)$.

There is a recursive word function $S(X,M,N)$ such that $S(X,M,N)$ is the word that results on replacing M by N at all of its occurrences in X. Thus

$$S([X \supset Y],M,N) \quad \text{is} \quad [S(X,M,N) \supset S(Y,M,N)]$$

and

$$S(\sim X,M,N) \quad \text{is} \quad \sim S(X,M,N)$$

If $i \neq j$, then

$$S((x_j)X,x_i,N) \quad \text{is} \quad (x_j)S(X,x_i,N)$$

There is a recursive word function $C(W)$. $C(W)$ is called the *closure of* W. If W is a wff, then $C(W)$ is a cwff, and $C(W)$ is obtained by prefixing zero or more universal quantifiers to W. If W is a cwff, then $C(W) = W$. If W is not a wff, then $C(W)$ is not a wff.

It follows that *the class of cwff's is recursive,* since W is a cwff if and only if $C(W) = W$, and there is a recursive procedure for recognizing equality.

4 *Integers*

a. Our final requirement of an arithmetical logic is that we be able to talk about numbers in it! To that end we wish to have words in our logic called the *numerals,* which will serve as the *names* of the integers. The idea of introducing numerals is to keep *things* and the *names of those things* separate—in a wff of our logic, it is not the number itself which appears, but rather the numeral which is the name of that number.

b. Associated recursively with each integer n is a word that we write n^* and that we call the numeral associated with the number n. If $n \neq m$, then $n^* \neq m^*$.

If A is a wff, if x_i is free in A, and if N is a variable or a numeral, then $S(A,x_i,N)$ is a wff.

If x_i is not bound in A, then

$$Th(L): [S(A,x_i,m^*) \supset (\exists x_i)A] \tag{5.4.3}$$

This completes our definition of an arithmetical logic. Thus, an *arithmetical logic* is a *recursive logic* equipped, in a fashion made precise above, with criteria for *well-formedness* of formulas, with propositional *connectives*, with universal and existential *quantifiers*, and with *numerals*.

We devote the remainder of this section to the concepts of ω-consistency, adequacy, and completeness.

Definition 5.4.1 A wff W of L is called *n-ary* if the variables $x_1, \ldots, x_n$ are free in W, and if no other variables are free in W. If W is an n-ary wff of L, and if $(y_1, \ldots, y_n)$ is an n-tuple of integers, we write $W(y_1^*, \ldots, y_n^*)$ to denote the wff obtained from W on replacing x_i by y_i^* at all occurrences of x_i in W, for $i = 1, 2, \ldots, n$.

We call a logic consistent if it is free from contradictions:

Definition 5.4.2 An arithmetical logic is called *consistent* if for no word A do we have both $Th(L)$: A and $Th(L)$: $\sim A$ (in other words, if it is not valid to both make and deny the same assertion within the logic).

Now, suppose $Th(L)$: $W(m^*)$ for $m = 0, 1, 2, 3, \ldots$. Even if we cannot prove $(x_i)\, W$ within L, we should certainly take it to be implied by the above list of theorems. Hence, we should take it as a contradiction if $Th(L)$: $\sim(x_i)W$. Thus ω-consistency is just as desirable as consistency, where

Definition 5.4.3 An arithmetical logic L is called *ω-consistent* if there does not exist a 1-ary wff W such that, for all integers m, $Th(L)$: $W(m^*)$ but also $Th(L)$: $\sim(x_i)W$.

Lemma 5.4.1 L is inconsistent if and only if all wff's of L are theorems.

Proof Suppose $Th(L)$: A and $Th(L)$: $\sim A$. Let B be any wff of L. We wish to show $Th(L)$: B.

By (5.4.1)	$Th(L): [\sim A \supset [\sim B \supset \sim A]]$
By modus ponens	$Th(L): [\sim B \supset \sim A]$
By (5.4.2)	$Th(L): [[\sim B \supset \sim A] \supset [A \supset B]]$
By modus ponens	$Th(L): [A \supset B]$
and hence	$Th(L): B$

The converse is, by definition, trivial. Q.E.D.

Corollary 5.4.2 If L is ω-consistent, then it is consistent.

We say that a predicate P is completely representable within a logic if we can always decide its truth or falsity, after substitution of constants, within the logic:

Definition 5.4.4 Let $P(x_1, \ldots, x_n)$ be a predicate. Then we say that P is *completely representable* in an arithmetical logic L if there exists an n-ary wff W of L such that—

a. For each n-tuple $(y_1, \ldots, y_n)$ of integers for which $P(y_1, \ldots, y_n)$ is true, $Th(L)$: $W(y_1^*, \ldots, y_n^*)$.
b. For each n-tuple $(y_1, \ldots, y_n)$ of integers for which $P(y_1, \ldots, y_n)$ is false, $Th(L)$: $\sim W(y_1^*, \ldots, y_n^*)$.

We now turn to the problem of defining what we require of a logic for it to be called adequate. We should like to be able to answer questions about recursively enumerable sets within such a logic, for we know that such sets are those which can be generated by a mechanical process and must thus interest the model maker, be he automata theorist, biologist, or engineer. We saw in Sec. 5.3 that a set of integers Q could be described in a recursive logic L only if it was recursively enumerable. In that case, we could hope that it was semicomplete wrt Q, i.e., that there existed a recursively enumerable set of words $W_0, W_1, W_2, \ldots$ such that $Q = \{n \mid Th(L): W_n\}$. If we are to accord a logic the title of adequacy, we might then require that it be semicomplete wrt *every* recursively enumerable set, i.e., that it represent every set that a recursive logic *can* represent!

In proving Theorem 5.3.1, we saw that the proofs of a recursive logic could be effectively enumerated. Bearing such an enumeration in mind, we can talk of the yth proof. Given our set Q and its set of words $\{W_0, W_1, W_2, \ldots\}$, let $R(x,y)$ be defined as the predicate "y is the number of a proof of W_x." Then if $R(x,y)$ is true, y is the number of a proof that x belongs to Q. Now, given x and y, we can effectively form W_x and effectively generate the yth proof and so effectively tell whether or not $R(x,y)$ is true. Hence $R(x,y)$ is a recursive predicate such that

$$Q = \{x \mid \text{there exists a } y \text{ such that } R(x,y) \text{ is true}\}$$

If we add to our requirement of adequacy that any *recursive* predicate be *completely representable*, we have sufficient motivation to at last give Davis's formal definition of adequacy:

Definition 5.4.5 An arithmetical logic L is called *adequate* if, for every recursively enumerable set Q, there is a predicate $R(x,y)$ completely representable in L, such that

$$Q = \{x \mid \text{there exists a } y \text{ such that } R(x,y) \text{ is true}\}$$

We may now make the final definition of this book. A logic is complete if the truth or falsity of every statement can be decided within the logic. More formally:

Definition 5.4.6 An arithmetical logic L is said to be *complete* if for every cwff A of L, either

$$Th(L): A \qquad \text{or} \qquad Th(L): \sim A$$

The proof of Gödel's Incompleteness Theorem follows simply in the next section.

5.5 The Proof of Gödel's Incompleteness Theorem

Theorem 5.5.1 (Gödel) If L is an ω-consistent and adequate arithmetical logic, then L is incomplete.

Proof By Theorem 1.6.3, we may choose Q to be a recursively enumerable set that is not recursive. Since L is adequate, there is a predicate $R(x,y)$, completely representable in L, such that

$$Q = \{x \mid \text{there exists a } y \text{ such that } R(x,y) \text{ is true}\} \qquad (5.5.1)$$

Thus there exists a 2-ary wff W such that when $R(x,y)$ is true,

$Th(L)\colon W(x^*,y^*)$

When $R(x,y)$ is false

$Th(L)\colon \sim W(x^*,y^*)$

Let U be the 1-ary wff $(\exists x_2)\ W$. We shall see that

$$Q = \{x \mid Th(L)\colon U(x^*)\} \qquad (5.5.2)$$

For each integer n, we write $W(n^*,x_2)$ for $S(W,x_1,n^*)$.

Now, suppose $n_0 \varepsilon Q$. Then, for some number y_0, $R(n_0,y_0)$ is true by (5.5.1). Hence $Th(L)\colon W(n_0^*,y_0^*)$. Now, by (5.4.3),

$Th(L)\colon [W(n_0^*,y_0^*) \supset (\exists x_2) W(n_0^*,x_2)]$

Hence, by modus ponens,

$Th(L)\colon (\exists x_2) W(n_0^*,x_2)$

That is,

$Th(L)\colon U(n_0^*)$

Conversely, suppose that $Th(L)\colon U(n_0^*)$. That is,

$Th(L)\colon (\exists x_2) W(n_0^*,x_2)$

or

$Th(L)\colon \sim(x_2) \sim W(n_0^*,x_2)$

Hence, by the ω-consistency of L, there is some integer m_0 for which the wff $\sim W(n_0^*,m_0^*)$ is not a theorem of L. Hence $R(n_0,m_0)$ must be true, since if it were false, we should have $Th(L)\colon \sim W(n_0^*,m_0^*)$. Hence, finally, $n_0 \varepsilon Q$, and we have proved

$$Q = \{x \mid Th(L)\colon U(x^*)\} \qquad (5.5.2)$$

Now, suppose that $Th(L)\colon \sim U(n^*)$. Then $n \varepsilon \bar{Q}$ (for if

$n \varepsilon Q$, $Th(L): U(n^*)$, which would contradict the consistency of L). Thus

$$\{x \mid Th(L): \sim U(x^*)\} \qquad \text{is a subset of } \bar{Q}$$

But by Corollary 5.3.3,

$$\{x \mid Th(L): \sim U(x^*)\} \neq \bar{Q}$$

since $\bar{Q}$ is *not* recursively enumerable. Hence there is a number n_0 such that $n_0 \varepsilon \bar{Q}$ but for which it is not the case that $Th(L): \sim U(n_0^*)$. On the other hand, it is also not the case that $Th(L): U(n_0^*)$, since this would imply $n_0 \varepsilon Q$. Hence $U(n_0^*)$ and $\sim U(n_0^*)$ are not decidable in L, and so L is incomplete. Q.E.D.

Now look at our proposition $\sim U(n_0^*)$. By (5.5.1) this is to be interpreted as $n_0 \varepsilon \bar{Q}$ and so *it is indeed a "true" statement.* And yet *it is not a theorem of* L; i.e., we have shown that if L is ω-consistent, there exists a true statement which cannot be proved in L. Further, one cannot escape this problem by merely adding $U(n_0^*)$ to that list of axioms, for the resultant logic L' is again subject to Gödel's theorem argument discussed above. Thus we can find a number n_1 such that $\sim U(n_1^*)$ is true, but is not a theorem of L', and so ad infinitum.

5.6 The Brain-Machine Controversy

Ernest Nagel and James R. Newman in their book "Gödel's Proof" state that Gödel's theorem definitely limits the mathematical power of computers. Let me quote some of their concluding remarks:

Gödel's conclusions bear on the question whether a calculating machine can be constructed that would match the human brain in mathematical intelligence. Today's calculating machines have a fixed set of directives built into them; these directives correspond to the fixed rules of inference of formalised axiomatic procedure. The machines thus supply answers to problems by operating in a step-by-step manner, each step being controlled by the built-in directives. But, as Gödel showed in his incompleteness theorem, there are innumerable problems in elementary number theory that fall outside the scope of a fixed axiomatic method, and that such engines are incapable of answering, however intricate and ingenious their built-in mechanisms may be, and however rapid their operations. The human brain may, to be sure, have built-in limitations of its own . . . [but Gödel's] theory does indicate that the structure and power of the human mind are far more complex and subtle than any non-living machine yet envisaged.

Having quoted Nagel and Newman on this topic, it is now only fair that I quote two others who disagree with them. Both quotations are from "Dimensions of Mind."†

Hilary Putnam in his article "Minds and Machines" says:

Let T be a Turing machine which "represents" me in the sense that T can prove just those statements I can prove. Then the argument [Nagel and Newman give no argument, but I assume they must have this one in mind] is that by using Gödel's technique I can discover a proposition that T cannot prove, and moreover *I* can prove the proposition. This refutes the assumption that T "represents" me, hence I am not a Turing machine. The fallacy is a misapplication of Gödel's Theorem, pure and simple. Given an arbitrary machine T, all I can do is find a proposition U such that *I* can prove:

If T is consistent, U is true, where U is undecidable by T if T is in fact consistent. However T can perfectly well prove this too, i.e., T can prove that U is undecidable by it, and that if T is consistent then U is "true" by the programmed interpretation. And the statement U, which T *cannot* prove (assuming consistency), *I* cannot prove either (unless I prove that T is consistent, which is unlikely if T is very complicated)!

To my mind, this refutation of Nagel and Newman is not completely satisfactory. A more satisfying reply is furnished by Michael Scriven in his "The Compleat Robot: A Guide to Androidology":

† Sydney Hook (ed.), Collier Books, a division of Crowell-Collier Publishing Co., New York, 1961.

Nagel and Newman are struck by the fact that whatever axioms and rules of inference one might give a computer, there would apparently be mathematical truths which it would never "reach" from these axioms by the use of these rules. This is true, but their assumption that we could suppose ourselves to have given the machine an adequate idea of mathematical truth when we give it the axioms and rules of inference is not true. This would be to suppose the formalists were right, and they were shown by Gödel to be wrong. The Gödel theorem is no more an obstacle to a computer than to ourselves. One can only say that mathematics would have been easier if the formalists had been right, and it would in that case be comparatively easy to construct a mechanical mathematician. They weren't and it isn't. But just as we can recognise the truth of the unprovable formula by comparing what it says with what we know to be the case, so can a computer do the same.

Anyone acquainted with modern-day computers is well aware that, as programmed at present, these machines are of negligible (if any) intelligence in comparison with a human being. The point of the above arguments is *not* to assert the intelligence of present machines, but rather to stress that *Gödel's theorem is not to be taken as a proof that no machine can be intelligent.* Our acquaintance with the perceptron in Sec. 2.2 and our brief glance at artificial intelligence in Sec. 4.5 should convince us that many of the intellectual limitations apparently inherent in computers can actually be removed by ingenious design and programming. The perceptron shows that a machine may adapt, artificial intelligence that a machine can be "creative," and servomechanisms that a machine can be purposive in its behavior. Admittedly, all this is at a far lower level than that exhibited by a human being, but it does demonstrate that many differences between man and machine which, until recently, have seemed immutably qualitative are merely quantitative.

Epilogue

In these chapters we have covered many experimental data and more or less related theories. Our field of study is vast, new, and fast-growing. Almost as rapid as the growth of the field has been the proliferation of names with which to designate it or its parts: cybernetics, bionics, neurodynamics, theory of self-organizing systems, artificial intelligence, etc. In this epilogue I shall pick "cybernetics" from this plethora and use it to denote the whole range of this book and not merely those topics which held our interest in Chap. 4. With the knowledge this book has given us of cybernetics *in this wide sense*, it is perhaps easy to feel overconfident. I think it is only fair then to give the reader a few warnings:

1. This material, by its very nature, must be only a personal sampling. None of the theories presented can be considered the final word on the subject. I can only hope that I have provided a not-too-biased view of the field and that this book will serve as a firm basis for any desired further reading.

2. Cybernetics is interdisciplinary. Thus, at its best, it allows a scientist the pleasure of working simultaneously in several fields—such as engineering, psychology, mathematics, and physiology. At its worst, it allows a not-very-good engineer to find refuge from his own problems by doing incompetent theoretical biology—his pride being saved because he knows too little biology to realize what a fool he is making of himself. If cybernetics is to shed all taint of pseudoscience, then people who work in it must be more than competent in at least one of the present-day divisions of science and really conversant with one or more other relevant ones. Teams of narrow specialists, too ignorant of one another's specialities to communicate effectively, cannot meet the need.

3. The reader who decides to plunge into the mass of technical literature (and, in particular, the many symposia) must keep his critical faculties alive to the fact that many of the papers contain exaggerated claims, technical errors, and ignorance of relevant fields.

4. In the first excitement over cybernetics, many people made overly generous predictions that by 1960 cybernetics would achieve various spectacular results, such as machine translation and the construction of artificial brains. Such overoptimism has led to overreaction, perhaps the outstanding example of which is the book "Computers and Common Sense . . ."† by Mortimer Taube. Taube's reaction is so strong that he compares the scientific status of cybernetics with that of astrology! Clearly, such an attitude would give the layman a very distorted view of cybernetics. Nevertheless, I recommend Taube's book to your careful attention. For when you can agree with his just criticisms and *provide your own arguments against his unjust criticisms* (*and there are many of them*), then you may be able to view the possibilities and limitations of cybernetics realistically.

Despite these warnings, this book attests to my feeling that much good work has been done under the banner of cybernetics.

† . . . , the Myth of Thinking Machines, Columbia University Press, New York, 1961.

The literature contains a hard core of competent papers which really add to our understanding of the common ground of "brains, machines, and mathematics," where mathematics is used to exploit analogies between the working of brains and the control-computation-communication aspects of machines. I believe that these papers constitute the kernel of a new, exciting, and valid extension of human knowledge.

Appendix: Basic Notions of Set Theory

We think of a *set* as merely a collection of objects (called its *elements*), be they points, numbers, or the states of a finite automaton.

If X has the elements x_1, x_2, x_3, . . . , we sometimes write $X = \{x_1,x_2,x_3, \ldots\}$.

By an abuse of language, we let ϕ denote the *empty set*, i.e., a set with no elements!

We use the notation $x \varepsilon X$ for "x is an element of the set X." Thus, if X is the set of even numbers, then we know that $2 \varepsilon X$, $4 \varepsilon X$, etc.

We use the notation $\{x \mid y\}$ for "the set of all x for which the statement y is true." Thus:

$$X = \{x \mid x \varepsilon X\}$$

The set of even numbers $= \{x \mid x = 2n \text{ for some integer } n\}$

If X and Y are two sets, we write $X \subset Y$ to indicate that X is a *subset* of Y, i.e., that every element of X is also an element of Y.

For example, for any set of X, we have $\phi \subset X$. If X and Y are two sets, then

$$
\begin{aligned}
X \cap Y &= \text{the } \textit{intersection} \text{ of } X \text{ and } Y \\
&= \{x \mid x \varepsilon X \textit{ and } x \varepsilon Y\} \\
&= \text{the set of elements common to } X \text{ and } Y \\
X \cup Y &= \text{the } \textit{union} \text{ of } X \text{ and } Y \\
&= \{x \mid x \varepsilon X \textit{ or } x \varepsilon Y\} \\
&= \text{the set of elements belonging to } X \text{ or } Y \text{ or both}
\end{aligned}
$$

If the X_a are a collection of sets, we let

$$
\begin{aligned}
\bigcup\{X_a \mid P(a)\} &= \{x \mid \text{there is an } a \text{ for which } P(a) \text{ is true and } x \varepsilon X_a\} \\
&= \text{the } \textit{union} \text{ of those } X_a \text{ for which } P(a) \text{ is true}
\end{aligned}
$$

If X and Y are two sets, then the *difference* $X - Y = \{x \mid x \varepsilon X$ and $x \not\varepsilon Y\}$ where $x \not\varepsilon Y$ means "x is not an element of Y."

Let $N = \{0,1,2,3, \ldots\}$ be the set of natural numbers. If $X \subset N$, then we define the *complement* of X as

$$
\begin{aligned}
\overline{X} &= N - X \\
&= \{x \mid x \text{ is an integer not in } X\}
\end{aligned}
$$

We use the notation $f : X \rightarrow Y$ for "f is a function from the set X to the set Y," i.e., "to each $x \varepsilon X$, f assigns an element $f(x) \varepsilon Y$." For example, if f is defined by $f(x) = x^2$, then $f : N \rightarrow N$.

If X is a subset of the integers, then the characteristic function of X, $C_X : N \rightarrow \{0,1\}$ is defined by

$$
C_X(x) = \begin{cases} 0 \text{ if } x \not\varepsilon X \\ 1 \text{ if } x \varepsilon X \end{cases}
$$

Given two sets X and Y, the *cartesian product* of X and Y

$$
\begin{aligned}
X \times Y &= \{(x,y) \mid x \varepsilon X \text{ and } y \varepsilon Y\} \\
&= \text{the set of ordered pairs in which the first element belongs to } X \text{ and the second to } Y
\end{aligned}
$$

For example, the cartesian plane is the cartesian product of the x axis and the y axis. If $f : X \times Y \rightarrow Z$, we write $f(x,y)$ rather than $f((x,y))$.

Index